Anthony Munday's
Zelauto: *The Fountaine of Fame*

Anthony Munday's

ZELAUTO

The Fountaine of Fame

1580

EDITED BY
Jack Stillinger

SOUTHERN ILLINOIS UNIVERSITY PRESS

CARBONDALE

CONTENTS

Anthony Munday's single original contribution to Elizabethan prose fiction appeared in 1580 with the following title page:

ZELAVTO. / ℈ THE FOVN- / taine of *Fame.* / *Erected in an Orcharde* / of Amorous Aduentures. / *Containing* / A Delicate *Disputation*, gallantly / discoursed betweene two noble / *Gentlemen of* Italye. / Giuen for a freendly entertainment / *to* Euphues, *at his late ariuall* / into England. / *By* A. M. *Seruaunt to the Right Ho-* / nourable the Earle of Oxenford. / Honos alit Artes. / ℊ *Imprinted at London by* Iohn / Charleuvood. 1580.

Chronologically it is the fifth or sixth of the Elizabethan novels, following Gascoigne's "The Adventures of Master F. J." (1573), Grange's *The Golden Aphroditis* (1577), Lyly's *Euphues. The Anatomy of Wyt* (1578), Gosson's *The Ephemerides of Phialo* (1579), and probably also Lyly's *Euphues and His England* (1580).[1] Never entered in the Stationers' Register,[2]

---

[1] The wording of its title page ("Giuen . . . *to* Euphues, *at his late ariuall* . . .") suggests that *Zelauto* was published after Lyly's second novel; but elsewhere (pp. 7, 180 in the present edition) Munday speaks of *welcoming* Euphues into England, and the possibility should not be overlooked, since both Munday and Lyly were "seruaunts" to the Earl of Oxford, and each presumably knew of the other's work in advance, that *Zelauto* appeared first.

[2] More than a hundred other titles were duly registered by Munday's publisher during the years 1575–85. Among uncertain entries for him, however, only one, "*certen newes of the Turk*" (29 October 1580), has

never reprinted, it survives in a single copy in the Bodleian Library.

Almost none of the early novels has been more neglected by scholars. J. J. Jusserand gave it a brief paragraph in *The English Novel in the Time of Shakespeare;*[3] J. W. H. Atkins (*The Cambridge History of English Literature*) and E. A. Baker (*The History of the English Novel*) mentioned only its title; and a 1913 article by Friedrich Brie showing that Part III of the novel contains an analogue to the bond story of *The Merchant of Venice*[4] drew little attention to it as a piece of fiction. In fact, the total body of criticism may be said to consist of three plot summaries and a few paragraphs on its style.[5] There is no scholarly or critical treatment corresponding to the articles on the novels of Gascoigne and Grange, or even to the criticism available on Gosson's *Ephemerides*, the only other of the early

---

even remote relevance to *Zelauto* (Edward Arber, *A Transcript of the Registers of the Company of Stationers of London,* II [London, 1875], 380). "Turkes" are mentioned twice in Part I, and all of Part II takes place among the Turks in Persia.

[3] Trans. Elizabeth Lee (London, 1890), pp. 147–48.

[4] "Zur Entstehung des 'Kaufmann von Venedig,'" *Jahrbuch der Deutschen Shakespeare-Gesellschaft,* XLIX, 97–121. The relationship between the two works, earlier pointed out by Francis Douce, *Illustrations of Shakspeare* (London, 1807), I, 280, has been subsequently discussed by Janet Spens, *An Essay on Shakespeare's Relation to Tradition* (Oxford, 1916), pp. 16–24, and by Celeste Turner [Wright], *Anthony Mundy: An Elizabethan Man of Letters* (Berkeley, 1928), pp. 32–34. (Mrs. Wright's biography is cited hereafter as "Turner.") See also John Russell Brown, ed., *The Merchant of Venice* (London, 1955), pp. xxx–xxxi, 156–68; Geoffrey Bullough, ed., *Narrative and Dramatic Sources of Shakespeare,* I (London, 1957), 452–54, 486–90; and Kenneth Muir, *Shakespeare's Sources,* I (London, 1957), 49, 50.

[5] Spens, pp. 17–22, and Turner, pp. 30–35, discuss style and give summaries; M. St. Clare Byrne, "Anthony Munday and His Books," *Library,* 4th ser., I (1921), 250–51, briefly treats style; René Pruvost, *Matteo Bandello and Elizabethan Fiction* (Paris, 1937), pp. 265–67, 274–76, summarizes the plot and quotes three pages of Part III as an example of "sentimental rhetoric."

novels not to have been reprinted.[6] The neglect of
Zelauto is, in part at least, undeserved.

Living as long as he did (1560–1633), Munday could
have written a string of books reflecting all the trends
in the course of Elizabethan fiction. As it is, he managed
to embody most of them in his one novel. The first of
the novelists who had no university training, he was
reading romances of chivalry, writing ballads, working
as a printer's apprentice, and possibly acting on the
stage while Lyly, Gosson, and others were absorbing
the euphuistic lectures of the Oxford Greek Reader
John Rainolds; [7] and he was outside England for a year
before he wrote the novel.[8] Largely because of these
facts, *Zelauto* differs in several ways from its predecessors. It is, to be sure, a euphuistic novel, but it is much
more than an imitation of Lyly's best sellers. Juxtaposed
with its euphuism and courtly love concerns are elements of chivalric romance and pastoralism, and even

[6] Percy Waldron Long, "From *Troilus* to *Euphues,*" *Anniversary
Papers by Colleagues and Pupils of George Lyman Kittredge* (Boston,
1913), pp. 367–76; Leicester Bradner, "The First English Novel: A Study
of George Gascoigne's *Adventures of Master F.J.,*" *PMLA*, XLV (1930),
543–52; Robert P. Adams, "Gascoigne's 'Master *F.J.*' as Original Fiction,"
PMLA, LXXIII (1958), 315–26; Hyder E. Rollins, "John Grange's *The
Golden Aphroditis,*" *Harvard Studies and Notes in Philology and Literature*, XVI (1934), 177–98; William Ringler, *Stephen Gosson: A Bio-
graphical and Critical Study* (Princeton, 1942), pp. 83–99.

[7] The details of Munday's early life are assembled by Mrs. Wright in
her biography (Turner, pp. 1–29) and in a recent article, "Young Anthony Mundy Again," *SP*, LVI (1959), 150–68. On Rainolds' influence
on the novelists see William Ringler's "The Immediate Source of Euphuism," *PMLA*, LIII (1938), 678–86, and his introduction to Walter
Allen's translation of Rainolds' *Oratio in laudem artis poeticae* (Princeton, 1940).

[8] Munday's trip to Italy in 1578–79, highly relevant to *Zelauto*, has been
discussed by Turner, pp. 16–23; by Miss Byrne, "The Date of Anthony
Munday's Journey to Rome," *Library*, 3rd ser., IX (1918), 106–15; and
by Beatrice Hamilton Thompson, "Anthony Munday's Journey to
Rome, 1578–9," *Durham University Journal*, XXXIV (1941), 1–14. Munday himself wrote a book on his travels, *The English Romayne Lyfe*
(1582), ed. G. B. Harrison, Bodley Head Quartos (London, 1925).

hints of the realism that became prominent in the fiction of the next decade.

In structure, *Zelauto* represents a considerable advance over the earlier novels. This is not to say that Munday deliberately planned an elaborate form, and in any event the novel is a fragmentary work, ending abruptly after Part III. Brought to completion, however, it could have been one of the most structurally sophisticated novels of the period. Its framework is established in the first ten or twelve pages of Part I. Zelauto, son of the Duke of Venice, leaves home on what is to be a six-year adventure in search of fame. Traveling first to Naples, then to Spain and Portugal, he meets a company of English merchants who describe their country and queen so attractively that he accompanies them home. He spends a year in England, and then departs for Persia. "In processe of time," Munday tells us, "he had visited many straunge Countryes, sustayned many and wonderfull iniuryes among the Turkes, which after shall be declared" (*p. 12*).[9] Arriving in Sicily in the sixth year of his travels, he encounters a savage hermit named Astraepho, who, after attacking him fiercely, becomes his "poore hoste" upon learning that he has tales of the world to tell. The two eat a midday meal, after which they discourse at length on the virtues of simple entertainment and contented living. Then Zelauto tells Astraepho the first of his adventures.

Such is the framework on which Munday arranges the stories that make up the bulk of the novel. In the remainder of Part I, Zelauto describes his travels from the beginning to the point at which he leaves England

[9] Parenthetical citations refer to pages in the present edition.

for Persia; Part I ends when the two men retire to
supper. Part II begins the next morning with Zelauto's
narration of his adventures in Persia, and ends when
Astraepho excuses himself to prepare dinner. To keep
Zelauto pleasantly occupied until dinnertime Astraepho
gives him a story to read. This "Delycate Deuise,"
which in itself has nothing to do with either Zelauto
or Astraepho, forms the whole of Part III, after which
the novel breaks off, and Munday informs the reader
he "shall haue the rest as possibilitie can permyt me." [10]
The structure in some ways resembles that of the
epic poem. Like Odysseus, Zelauto is well toward the
end of his travels when the story begins. Somewhat
like Homer's hero, he lands on an island and is dis-
covered by one of its inhabitants, to whom he relates his
past adventures, the telling of which constitutes the
greater portion of the work. Completing his story,
Munday would have brought Zelauto's adventures up
to date, and then described his journey home and re-
ception there. The digressive tale of Part III (which
seems to have been included only to extend the work
to book length) might, in this hypothetical over-all
scheme, be considered no more damaging to the unity
of the work than the similar digressions characteristic of
the epic.

[10] The reader lacks not only the rest of Zelauto's narration, but Astraepho's own "straunge aduentures" that he promises to tell (p. 20)
when Zelauto has finished. Munday's explanation at the end of his dedicatory epistle—"The last part of this woorke remaineth vnfinished, the
which for breuity of time, and speedines in the Imprinting: I was constrained to permit till more limited leysure"—suggests that *Zelauto* was
hurriedly produced and designed either to anticipate (and thereby to
advertise) or to profit from the success of Lyly's second novel (see
note 1, above). That the novel was never completed may be attributed
to its unpopularity or to the fact that Munday shortly afterward became involved in pamphlet warfare concerning the stage, Catholic agents
in England, and his own activities in Rome.

Although Zelauto's adventures are not especially interesting, Munday presents them skillfully. Mingled
with Zelauto's narration of the past there is constant
reference to his situation in the present: Zelauto may
stop his tale to ask Astraepho's judgment in some matter,
or Astraepho may interrupt with a question or a few
words of admiration. We never forget that it is Zelauto,
not Munday, who is telling the story, and that Zelauto's
adventures are not complete, like those of the narrators
of Utopias, but are still in progress, since he has yet to
get from Sicily back to his father's court. The frequent
transitions from past to present also enable Munday to
pass smoothly from one incident to another, and to
skip whatever intervening details he wishes to avoid.

The most obvious fault of the structure is the repe-
tition that it produces. Zelauto relates to Astraepho
some of the facts that Munday has already given the
reader in establishing the framework of the novel, and
Zelauto repeats some of these details once or twice
within the stories that he tells to Astraepho. But re-
gardless of its success or failure, the structure in 1580
was the most ambitious in Elizabethan fiction. Taking
into consideration the tale of Part III, we have three
levels of narrative in the novel: Munday tells the entire
story to the reader; within Munday's story there is
Zelauto's narration to Astraepho and their dialogue;
finally there is the narrative of Part III, a story which
Astraepho has written down and which, through Zelauto's "perusal" of it, is relayed to the reader of the
novel. A similar narrative complexity does not appear
in Elizabethan fiction until Nashe's *The Unfortunate
Traveller*, fourteen years later.

Zelauto's adventures, as he describes them to Astraepho, may be detailed here in brief space. Outside Naples, he encounters outlaws who wound him, rob him of clothes and money, and slay his companion. He manages to crawl into the city, where "At last, hauing espyed an *Osteria:* I boldly entered, putting my selfe in the handes of God, to whome I referred the paying of my charges" (*p. 21*). The hostess of the inn, Mistress Ursula, gives him the best room in the house, entertaining him elegantly despite the fact that he has no money. With pleasant discourse Zelauto and Ursula pass the time necessary for his recovery; she sings him a love song, hinting that he is to interpret it literally. When fully healed, he departs, having secured money and another companion through a friend living in Naples, and quickly travels to Valencia, Seville, and Lisbon, where he comes upon the merchants with whom he sails to England. In London he is received by a fellow countryman, and introduced by him to gentlemen of the English court. After a time he sees Queen Elizabeth, and attends some pageants and tournaments given for her. Having told this much, Zelauto reads to Astraepho an account he has written of a tournament in which an armed lady challenges and unhorses a knight who has disparaged the queen's beauty. He recites verses that he wrote in praise of the queen and "a certayne Noble Lorde" (the Earl of Oxford), and then tells that he reluctantly left England to continue his travels. Part I concludes with his promise to tell of "the myseries that I poore soule abode among the tyrannous *Turkes.*"

Dealing with only one incident, the second part is less rambling and correspondingly more interesting. Zelauto arrives in heathen Persia and lodges at an inn where the hostess is a Florentine and a Christian, and her husband a prospective convert to Christianity. Losing no time, he is well along toward effecting the host's conversion when Mica Sheffola, a nephew to the Sultan, enters the inn, lamenting that his sister has been condemned to die the next morning for "her Christian beleefe, and constant auouching of the same" (*p. 76*). Hearing that the Sultan has offered to free her if any champion can defeat his son in a trial of arms, Zelauto agrees to come forward with a challenge. On the morrow he enters the lists, and after a lengthy speech slays his opponent. The Sultan puts him and his host into prison under sentence of death. The host is hanged the next morning, but Zelauto is rescued by Mica Sheffola, who arranges his escape and sends him toward Constantinople with money and a new companion. Part II, with all that we hear of Zelauto's adventures, ends at this point.

I have found no specific literary sources for Parts I and II, although the events in them are so simple that none is needed. General similarities to *Euphues* and its sequel readily suggest themselves: both Zelauto and Euphues are young noblemen who leave home to see the world; both visit Naples and eventually England, where they are struck with admiration for the queen. But resemblances in plot go no further. More important are the details that came from Munday's own experience, especially from his trip to Italy in the year before the novel was published. Of the various reasons claimed for this journey, only Munday's need concern us.[11] As stated in *The English Romayne Lyfe* (1582), his purpose was "to see straunge Countreies, as also affection

---

[11] His enemies accused him of going as a spy to betray the English seminary at Rome. Modern scholars, following Thomas Seccombe in the *DNB*, generally suggest that he went in order to make literary capital

to learne the languages . . . and not any other intent or cause." [12] Zelauto gives more or less the same reason for his travels five times in the novel. Zelauto's encounter with Neapolitan outlaws is based on Munday's own experience with a group of disbanded soldiers who attacked him and left him stripped and moneyless shortly after he landed on the continent. At various times Zelauto calls on his countrymen in foreign lands, receives money by means of letters, and falsifies his identity, all of which Munday did during his journey. Zelauto is handsomely treated whenever he stops at an inn, and even in Persia he gets "the best and pleasauntest Chamber in the prison" (*p. 100*); these details, along with Ursula's charge against "common Inholders, and those tipling Tauerners" (*pp. 26–27*) in a discourse with Zelauto, reflect Munday's less fortunate experiences in traveling from inn to inn on the continent.[13] The entire episode of what might be called the Christian underground in Persia roughly parallels Munday's experiences among Catholics in Rome. Finally, the brief description of the execution and mutilation of Zelauto's Persian host (*p. 102*) could have been suggested by several executions that Munday witnessed in London and Rome; the scenes in which the condemned lady is led to her death (*p. 87*) and Zelauto escapes from prison (*pp. 104–05*) are also well enough detailed to have come from personal observation or experience.

---

out of whatever he could learn to the detriment of the English Catholics abroad. Mrs. Wright, however (*SP*, LVI [1959], 155), thinks that "Since his master [John Allde] and his publisher [John Charlewood] worked for Catholic noblemen, and his patron [Oxford] was a crypto-Catholic, there is now little doubt that he went as a convert, not a spy."

[12] Ed. G. B. Harrison (London, 1925), p. 2.

[13] All these details may be found in Chapter I of *The English Romayne Lyfe*, pp. 1–17.

Munday's acquaintance with chivalric romances enters significantly into the novel.[14] Zelauto's quest for fame, with its six-year time limit, is a chivalric motif, as is the standard set of questions—name, nation, and parentage—that he is asked many times in the course of his travels. Two knightly contests, conducted with all the standard formalities, occur in the novel, one between the armed lady and the rude knight who discredits Elizabeth's beauty, the other between Zelauto and the Sultan's son. Might is equated with right, as often in the romances, when the loser of the first contest is forced to realize that he held a wrong opinion; and much is made, after the second contest, of the Sultan's violation of a law of arms by punishing Zelauto for slaying his opponent in a fair fight. Munday is the first Elizabethan novelist to use themes and incidents from the chivalric romance, themes that become prominent a few years late in Sidney's *Arcadia* and, less happily, in the novels of Emanuel Ford. Not the least of the influences of the chivalric romance is a formal one: *Zelauto* is the earliest English novel to have chapter divisions.[15]

[14] His translations of chivalric romances, which he turned out in volume after volume from around 1578 until a decade or so before his death, perhaps constitute his most important influence on English literature. See Gerald R. Hayes, "Anthony Munday's Romances of Chivalry," *Library*, 4th ser., VI (1925), 57–81, VII (1926), 31–38; "The Chronology of Mundy's Romances" in Turner, pp. 180–83; and the many references to Munday in Mary Patchell, *The "Palmerin" Romances in Elizabethan Prose Fiction* (New York, 1947), and in Henry Thomas, *Spanish and Portuguese Romances of Chivalry* (Cambridge, Eng., 1920). At the beginning of the dedicatory epistle in *Zelauto* Munday alludes to several names and incidents of the Palmerin cycle; at its close he promises Oxford that shortly his translation of "the renowned *Palmerin* of England with all speede shall be sent you" (see the explanatory note to 6:19). Two minor characters in the novel, Pollinarda and Oriana, are named after heroines of the Palmerin cycle and *Amadis of Gaul*.

[15] The chapters of Parts I and II are designated by long descriptive headings; in addition to these, chapter numbers are used in Part III.

Munday also sounds the first pastoral note in English fiction—again, however, primarily under the influence of the continental romances, in which pastoralism was increasingly intermixed with the old chivalric themes. Zelauto's and Astraepho's several discourses on contented living and the virtues of simple, rural life as contrasted with the vanity and superfluity of courtly life are stock themes of the Renaissance pastoral. Astraepho has deliberately renounced the life of a courtier, and Zelauto, like Sir Calidore in *The Faerie Queene*, comes very close to doing the same thing. The ending of Part I, when Astraepho says "it draweth now towarde night. . . . Let vs now goe in, and prouide something for our Supper," is a standard pastoral termination; and the following outburst by Astraepho embodies a common pastoral motif: "Now to the sprouting sprayes I commend my sute, the Hylles, the Dales, the Rockes, the Clyffes, the Cragges, yea, and the gallant Ecchoes resound of this solitary Wyldnesse, they and none but they can witnesse of my woe" (*p. 63*).

Other influences may be seen. The great body of courtesy literature, for example, lies behind one long discourse on hospitality (*pp. 26–27*), two passages touching the proper conduct of princes (*pp. 9, 89–90*), and a discussion of the relationship between virtue and nobility (*p. 46*); almost no word is used more often by Zelauto than "courtesy." A single instance of the courtly love influence so pervasive in Part III appears in Part I when Munday adapts the phraseology of the love plaint to the armed lady's extravagant praise of the queen: "What dooth the Gods delude mee? or hath the infernall ghosts enchaunted me with their fonde illusions? Wake I, or sleepe I? See I, or see I not? What chaunce hath conuicted me? What sodayne sight hath attaynted me? Is this a Goddesse, or a mortall creature?" (p. 41). Essentially, however, Parts I and II are the product of euphuistic plot, Munday's own experience, chivalric romance, and (if it can be separated from the romance) the pastoral.

While Part III, the "Amorous discourse" that Astraepho gives Zelauto to read, is more skillfully connected to the rest of the novel than Lyly's extraneous material in *Euphues*, it is nevertheless entirely different from the other two parts.[16] It was probably written earlier; otherwise it would be difficult to explain why Munday devoted his time to a new story instead of completing Zelauto's adventures. On the other hand, as a piece of fiction it is much more sophisticated than Parts I and II. To a certain extent it has a literary source in a way in which the others apparently do not.

The hero of the story is Strabino, son of a gentleman of Pescara, who goes to Verona to be trained in one of the academies. There he becomes sworn brother of a fellow student, Rodolfo, whose sister Cornelia is "in all poynts so well proportioned: that the lookes of her Amorous countenaunce, infected in the heart of *Strabino* . . . a Feuer so fantasticall: that none but only shee must be the curer thereof" (*p. 114*). He finds himself in the worst agonies of love, but soliloquy and discourse bring him no remedy. Meanwhile another wooer, Signor Truculento, an old and miserly usurer of the city, visits Cornelia's father, Signor Ruscelli, bringing costly gifts to forward his suit for her hand in marriage.

---

[16] It is also considerably longer. Parts I, II, and III occupy 51, 40, and 52 pages respectively in the 1580 quarto, but Parts I and II were enlarged with twenty-three woodcuts (see the explanatory note to 61:18), while Part III contained no illustrations.

Ruscelli, "beeing one him selfe that preferred money before manly modestie" (*p. 148*), readily accepts Truculento's proposal. Cornelia vows death before such a match, but Ruscelli promises the dismayed Truculento that she will change her mind.

Cornelia accepts Strabino's suit shortly afterward, explaining that she rejected him earlier only for fear that he "might haue alleadged my minde to be lyght" (*p. 153*). Following her plan to appease her father and serve Truculento as he deserves, Strabino borrows four thousand ducats from Truculento, buys Ruscelli a jewel, and gains his consent to their marriage. Rodolfo woos and wins Truculento's daughter, Brisana, and the two couples celebrate a double wedding, momentarily forgetful of the bond that both young husbands have signed, involving not only the forfeiture of their lands but the loss of both their right eyes if Strabino fails to repay Truculento on time.

Enraged to learn that he has been tricked out of daughter, ducats, and marriage with Cornelia, Truculento hales Strabino and Rodolfo into court for nonpayment of the debt. Strict justice is to be administered, Truculento will have his bond, and the two young men are about to lose their eyes when Cornelia and Brisana, attired as scholars, come forward in court to defeat Truculento through legal technicalities. Seeing no remedy, Truculento accepts Rodolfo as his son-in-law. "Thus were they on all partes verie well pleased, and euerie one accoumpted him selfe well contented" (*p. 180*).

Chiefly three types of literature underlie this story. The first, courtly love romance, which Munday inherited as a part of the chivalric tradition, is one of the commonest phenomena in Renaissance literature. In a thesis on the euphuistic novel, John Weld has given a formula for this kind of romance as it appears subsequently in English:

> Typically a young man meets a young woman and is ensnared by her beauty. With the artful aid of schemata and his commonplace book he tells her of his love. She fears to be thought too forward and rejects him, reminding him of the faithlessness of Jason, Theseus, and Aeneas. A *debat d'amour* may be held, allowing the hero to display his knowledge of natural and classical history. The characters retire to their respective chambers for euphuistic self-analysis. Then like a valiant soldier unwilling to be daunted by the first repulse, the hero again pleads his love by letter, poem, or speech. So it goes.[17]

Weld's formula essentially describes what happens in the first half of Munday's story.

The second type of literature underlying the story is the jestbook, which affects not only incident and character, but style, as I shall point out later. The verbal trickery with which Strabino wins Signor Ruscelli's consent is typical of the way in which jestbook situations are resolved. He presents Ruscelli with a jewel, and secures a promise from him for a jewel in return. The jewel he seeks is, of course, Cornelia. Perceiving his object, Ruscelli tries to back out of the agreement; but when Strabino holds him to his promise, he can only give his blessing to the couple. The aged and comic wooer Truculento is a stock jestbook character, and

---

[17] John Weld, "Studies in the Euphuistic Novel (1576–1640)" (unpub. diss., Harvard, 1940), p. 144.

Cornelia, with all her cleverness, exhibits some of the characteristics of the jestbook heroine.

It is difficult to tell just where the jestbook influence ends and the third influence, that of the Italian novella, takes over, for the two have much in common.[18] The novella is at least responsible for the bond story. Munday's specific source, like Shakespeare's in *The Merchant of Venice*, is not known. It was some form of the pound-of-flesh story, of which Giovanni Fiorentino's version in *Il Pecorone* is the most familiar example. Two scholars suggest that Munday may have seen a dramatized version, perhaps the play mentioned by Gosson in 1579 called *"The Jew* . . . representing the greedinesse of worldly chusers and the bloody minds of usurers."* [19] Munday's biographer has praised his version of the story for representing Truculento as a Christian instead of a Jew, thus enabling him to play rival suitor to Strabino.[20] But although this modification gives him a good motive for his hatred once he is tricked, it destroys his motive for making the gruesome bond in the first place, when he still looks on Rodolfo, Strabino's surety, as a potential brother-in-law. Indeed, the chief weakness of the story is that Rodolfo himself not only volunteers the terms of the bond, but almost has to argue Truculento into agreement. Munday handles the point so clumsily as to suggest that making the villain a Christian was his own idea.

[18] As a further complication, one might add a fourth general influence, that of the Italian *commedia erudita*, on which see Marvin T. Herrick, *Italian Comedy in the Renaissance* (Urbana, Ill., 1960), pp. 60–164.

[19] Turner, p. 34, and Spens, pp. 23–24. Miss Spens's suggestion that Munday himself wrote the lost play will not hold up when the dates of his Italian journey and the extent of his literary production after returning to England are considered.

[20] Turner, p. 34.

Munday's style and ability in characterization remain to be discussed. Since *Zelauto* is usually listed among imitations of *Euphues*, it would be worth while to examine the extent of Munday's debt to Lyly. As its title page, epistle to the reader, and closing salutation proclaim, *Zelauto* was written to welcome Euphues into England; and Munday urges the reader to "like that *Lilly* whose sent is so sweete, and fauour his freend who wisheth your welfare" (*p. 8*). Apart from these allusions, however, there is little connection between the two, beside the general similarities in plot that I have already mentioned. If Munday tried to imitate Lyly's style, he succeeded only superficially. Certainly *Zelauto* was written in the same oratorical-dramatic tradition as *Euphues*. There are the formal orations and debates that derive from the rhetoric books, Italian courtesy literature and social customs, and imitations of the Platonic dialogue. The first two parts of the novel are printed as dialogue, generally with the speaker's name above each speech. But where Lyly makes moral treatises of his discourses, Munday more often than not has Zelauto tell of his adventures, so that his novel has considerably more action than Lyly's two novels combined.

As a rule the speeches in *Zelauto* are shorter than those in *Euphues*, and at times, especially in Part III, the dialogue becomes quite terse, as, for example, when Strabino tells Cornelia that a picture of his beloved is framed in the mirror he holds in his hand:

And haue you found her face there (quoth she). I pray you let me see her, to iudge if I know her. After *Cornelia* had looked a whyle, she sayd. Why *Strabino*, you promised I should see that seemely shee, to whom you owe such delightfull looue and loyaltie. And what

I promised (quoth he) hath beene heere performed.
As how (quoth she). Whose face (quoth he) did you
behold when I shewed you? Why yours and mine
owne (quoth she). I thought it would come to such
a passe, well I will speake to her, and if she chaunce to
giue her consent: doubt you not but you shall heare of
it. (*pp. 131–32*)

One would search far to find similar brevity in the
earlier euphuistic novels. Even Munday's lengthiest
discourses—those on excess, hospitality, religion, love
—are shorter, less learned, less involved than Lyly's.

A comparison of the two novelists' eulogies of Elizabeth will illustrate some of their differences. Euphues'
admiration for the queen runs to six pages in the Bond
edition, and consists of purely abstract praise, as unin-
formative as it is tedious. Zelauto, on the other hand,
says, "because I am vnable to paynt foorth her passing
prayse, according as desert deserueth: I remyt her vnder
the vayle of Eternall memorie, to the graue iudgement
of others" (*pp. 36–37*)—and his eulogy nearly ends at
its outset. Astraepho, of course, begs further description; yet the burden of Zelauto's tribute is carried in the
story of the armed lady and the rude knight and in a
poem of twenty-four lines that says as much as Lyly's
six pages. Munday, moreover, supplies at least one fac-
tual detail: both writers praise the queen's linguistic
ability, but where Lyly passes on to another topic Munday adds the following:

Also, it is not vnknowen, howe her Princely Maiestie
made the minde of the valiant *Marques Vitelli* (Ambassador sent from the King of *Spayne*) to be marueylously mooued. This *Vitelli*, hath bene knowen a excellent warriour, and yet the rare excellencie of this

Queene had almost put him cleane out of conceyt. That as he sayde him selfe: he was neuer so out of countenaunce before any Prince in all his lyfe. (*p. 37*)

Munday's prose style is euphuistic to the extent that he uses alliteration, balance, and antithesis, strings of rhetorical questions, and proverbs and sententiae. There are none of the zoological similes characteristic of Pettie's and Lyly's writings, and classical and historical allusions are used more sparingly. Munday was not so clever as Lyly; consequently his prose is less artful and, as it happens, more lifelike. Elements of humor, entirely lacking in Lyly's work, result from the influences of the jestbook and Italian novella, as in the following description of Truculento:

The olde horson would needes be lusty, and to cheerishe vp his churlishe carkase, would get him a wanton Wife. And though I say it, he was as well made a man, and as curious in his quallities: as euer an olde Horse in this towne, when he is gnabling on a thystle. This carpet Knight, hauing pounced him selfe vp in his perfumes, and walking so nice on the ground, that he would scant bruse an Onion: comes to the house of *Signor Giorolamo Ruscelli.* (*p. 146*)

Ruscelli's final dismissal of Truculento exhibits at once the balance of euphuism and the racy diction of the jestbook: "If you set not a poynt by vs: we care not a pyn for you, if we may haue your good will so it is: if not, keepe your winde to coole your Pottage" (*p. 169*). In his occasional use of colloquial diction and rapid dialogue in Part III, Munday looks forward to the sort of realism to be found in the novels of Deloney.

The many proverbs in *Zelauto*, which could have

come mainly from John Heywood's *Dialogue* (1546) but occasionally also from Erasmus by way of translations like Richard Taverner's *Proverbes* (1539) and Nicholas Udall's *Apophthegmes* (1542), were the common property of Elizabethan writers. Munday's classical and historical learning could have come from a variety of sources, including contemporary reference dictionaries, Latin quotation books, and Thomas North's translation of Plutarch, published in 1579. The concentration of proverbs and historical allusions in the discourses on wealth and excess suggests that Munday may have referred to his own (now lost) *"Defence of pouertie against the Desire of worldlie riches Dialogue wise,"* licensed by Charlewood on 18 November 1577.[21] Most, perhaps all, of the allusions and similes that Munday used can be found in other English works, but not very many of them occur in any single earlier work. He borrowed almost nothing from Lyly or Pettie.[22] One most reasonably would suppose that he worked from his commonplace book rather than from any specific printed source.

Like the novelists who preceded him, Munday was no master of characterization. Most of the characters in *Zelauto* are voices instead of people; minor characters like the three or four knights who accompany Zelauto are forgotten as soon as they are introduced. Generally

[21] Arber, II, 320.

[22] While Munday and Lyly or Pettie sometimes cite the same classical or historical names, their allusions are dissimilar. An exception is the allusion to Timanthes and Agamemnon's portrait (p. 36 of the present edition; *The Complete Works of John Lyly*, ed. R. Warwick Bond [Oxford, 1902], II, 22); but Lyly names the artist *"Tamantes,"* Munday *"Timon"* (corrected in the errata to read *"Timantes"*). Alluding (p. 144) to Pygmalion and Admetus, the heroes of Pettie's eleventh and sixth tales, Munday has the latter (instead of his beloved Alcestis) disguised in man's attire. In proverbs common to Munday and Lyly or Pettie, Munday's wording invariably follows some earlier writer's version.

the characters of Part III are more acceptable, owing no doubt to a difference in sources and influences. Zelauto is given some individuality. Indistinguishable from Euphues at first, he becomes less heroic and more like his practical author as the novel progresses. Addressing the Persian Sultan, he shows unwillingness to risk his life for the condemned lady: "I thinke it sufficient that you put her in exyle, with expresse charge in payne of death neuer to returne: so may your rigor be verie well asswaged, and shee for her paines indifferently penaunced" (p. 92). After describing the reluctance with which he killed the Sultan's son, he tells Astraepho: "But as you know your selfe, a man in such affayres, dealeth as best he can, for the sauegarde of him selfe, is his cheefest desire" (p. 97). Munday did not learn such practicality from the romances of chivalry. Cornelia, however, who in some ways compares well with Deloney's women, is the only real character of the novel. Gay, sprightly, and much more clever than Strabino, whose awkward advances she sees through immediately, she defies and out-argues her father in refusing to marry Truculento, and initiates the action that ultimately satisfies her father and foils Truculento. Presenting a somewhat realistic contrast to Strabino's courtly manner, she joins the stereotyped love plot of the first half of the story with the jestbook-novella situation of the last half. It is largely through her that Munday achieves his best dialogue.

Taking an over-all view of this hurriedly produced, unfinished work, one must say, finally, that its combination of such disparate influences as euphuism, chivalric romance, the pastoral, courtly love, the jestbook, and the novella, results at times in an almost fantastic disunity of style, tone, and theme. Though it has more action and at least one better character than Lyly's novels can show, it is easily surpassed in every respect by later novels, while *Euphues* remains the epitomizing example of euphuistic prose. *Zelauto* apparently had almost no influence on later fiction,[23] certainly none comparable to the influence that Munday's translations exerted. For all its mediocrity, however, the facts remain that its structure is an artistic improvement over the straightforward narrative plan of the novels that preceded it; that its combination of chivalric romance and pastoral motifs anticipates such really significant works as Sidney's *Arcadia* and Lodge's *Rosalynde;* and that its occasional passages of jestlike humor, colloquial diction, and rapid dialogue mark the beginning of the shift away from the artificiality of euphuism toward the realistic manner that was to flourish in the works of Nashe and Deloney. These are reasons enough for reprinting the novel.

THE TEXT

From my copy-text, which is, of course, the single extant copy of *Zelauto*, in the Bodleian Library, I have departed in the following particulars: *1*] The typography of the original is not strictly followed. Roman type is generally used as the standard, but the dedicatory epistle, chapter headings, marginal glosses, and poems are printed in italic. In the original, the dedicatory epistle is printed in italic, the address "To the well disposed Reader" in black letter, and "The Argument" in roman;

---

[23] Weld, p. 22, suggests that *Zelauto* furnished certain plot details in Henry Roberts' *A Defiance to Fortune* (1590).

thereafter the text is in black letter, except for chapter headings, poems, and Munday's further addresses to the reader, at the beginning and end of Part II and the beginning of Part III—all of which are in roman. My italics (and roman type in the chapter headings and marginal glosses) represent either roman type within italic or black letter, or italic within roman or black letter.[24] 2] The ampersand and other abbreviations ("y{e}" = "the," "y{t}" = "that," as well as the tilde representing an omitted "m" or "n" after a vowel) are silently expanded; and modern "s" (for "ſ") and "w" (for "vv," both capital and lower case) are used throughout. 3] The occurrence of random italic, small-capital, and wrong-fount letters is ignored, along with some other purely typographical peculiarities—for example, the ligatured double "e" (so that for the 1580 "seͤeth" I give "seeeth"). 4] In chapter headings, where (owing to the printer's lack of a certain size of italic type) the practice of the original varies, the names of characters and places are consistently set off by roman type within italic. 5] In marginal glosses the frequent absence of hyphens dividing words between lines is not noticed, and periods are silently added to the ends of glosses where they are lacking. In all other respects I have either followed the copy-text faithfully, or recorded my departures in the List of Emendations, which, because I have altered conservatively and the list is short, contains substantive emendations as well as corrections of misprints. A few questionable emendations are discussed in the Explanatory Notes.

[24] I should perhaps add that pages 1, 59, and 109, though they follow the wording and punctuation of the original, are in no sense intended as facsimile titles.

I wish to thank the Bodleian Library for permission to reprint *Zelauto*, and my colleague Gwynne Blakemore Evans for many helpful suggestions in the editing. Mr. J. A. Brister, of the Bodleian, very kindly checked a number of questionable readings for me.

Zelauto.

The Fountaine of Fame.

Erected in an Orcharde of Amorous Aduentures.
Containing A Delicate Disputation, gallantly
discoursed betweene two noble Gentlemen of
Italye. *Giuen for a freendly entertain-*
ment to Euphues, *at his late ariuall*
into England. By A. M. Seruaunt
to the Right Honourable
the Earle of Oxenford.

Honos alit Artes.

¶ Imprinted at London by *Iohn Charlewood. 1580.*

TO THE RIGHT HONORABLE, HIS

singuler good Lord and Maister, Edward de Vere,
Earle of Oxenford, Viscount Bulbeck, Lord Sand-
ford, and of Badelesmere, and Lord high
Chamberlaine of England, Antony
Munday, *wisheth all happines*
in this Honorable estate,
and after death eter-
nall life.

AFTER *that the Englishe Prince*
(Right Honorable and my verie
good Lord) had taken view of the
seemelye Portrature of Gridonia,
her tender Infant lying by her, and
leading two Lions in her hand: he presently left
the Court, and tooke himselfe to trauayle. When
the princely Primaleon, *heard pronounced before*
his famous father the Emperour of Constantinople,
the sorrowfull Letters sent by the Lady of the
Lake, *how his best belooued brother was loste in*
the vnfortunate Forest of England: *he abandoned*
all his Courtly delights, and neuer ceassed wan-
dring, till he became prisoner in the same place.
So my simple selfe (Right Honourable) hauing
sufficiently seene the rare vertues of your noble
minde, the heroycall quallities of your prudent
person: thought, though abilitie were inferiour to
gratifie with some gift, yet good will was ample to

bestowe with the best. When all the braue Gallants *and woorthy* Gentlemen *in* Roome, *presented vnto the* Emperour Iewels *and gifts of great value and estimation: a poore* Cittizen *amongst them all brought a handfull of* Flowers, *and offered them to the* Emperour, *the which he receiued gratiously and with great affection, and gaue him a great reward. Why (quoth one of the* Gentlemen) *how durst thou presume to giue so poore a present, to so puissant a person? Why (quoth the* Citizen) *how durst they be so bolde to giue such great gifts? Quoth the* Gentleman, *they are of great credit, and beside, their gifts woorthy the receiuing. And I am poore (quoth the* Cittizen) *and therefore I giue such a meane gift, yet hath it beene gratefully accepted: And although they discend of such noble Linages: yet doo they owe dutifull alleageaunce vnto the* Emperour, *and as poore as I am, I beare him as true a heart as the best: Euen so my poore gift hath beene as faithfully deliuered: as the richest Iewell that was by them presented.*

And loe Right Honourable, among such expert heads, such pregnaunt inuentions, and such commendable writers, as preferre to your seemely selfe, woorkes woorthy of eternall memory: A simple Soule, *(more imboldened on your clemencie, then any action whatsoeuer he is able to make manifest) presumeth to present you with such vnpullished practises: as his simple skill is able to comprehend. Yet thus much I am to assure your Honour, that among all them which owe you dutifull seruice, and among all the braue* Bookes *which haue beene bestowed: these my little labours containe so much faithfull zeale to your wel-*

fare, as others whatsoeuer, I speake without any excepcion. But least that your Honour should deeme I forge my tale on flatterie, and that I vtter with my mouth, my hart thinketh not: I wish for the tryall of my trustinesse, what reasonable affayres your Honour can best deuise, so shall your minde be deliuered from doubt: and my selfe rid of any such reproche. But as the puissantest Prince is not voyde of enemies, the gallantest Champion free from foes, and the moste honest liuer without some backbiters: euen so the brauest Bookes hath many malicious iudgements, and the wisest writers not without rashe reports. If then (Right Honourable) the moste famous are found fault withall, the cuningest controlled, and the promptest wits reproched by spitefull speeches: how dare so rude a writer as I, seeme to set foorth so meane a matter, so weake a woorke, and so skillesse a stile? When the learned are deluded: I must needes be mocked, and when the skilfullest are scorned: I must needes be derided: But yet I remember, the wise will not reprehend rashly, the learned condemne so lightly, nor the courteous misconster the good intent of the writer: But onely sutch as Æsops Dog, that brags but dares not bite, hid in a hole and dare not shewe their heads, against all such, the countenaunce of your Honour is sufficient to contend, which makes me not feare the force of their enuie. The Chirurgion more douteth the hidden Fistule: then the wide wound, the woorthiest warriour more feareth the secret assault: then the boldest battaile, A little hooke taketh a great Fish, a little winde falleth downe big fruit, a smal spark kindleth to a great fire, a little stone may make a tall man stumble, and a small wound kill a puissant person: Euen so the hidden enemy may sooner harme a man: then when he trieth his quarrell face to face, and the least report of a slaundrous toung (beeing lightly beleeued) may discredit him to his vtter vndooing. But for my part I feare not, let them prate at their pleasure, and talke till their toungs ake, your Honour to please, is the cheefe of my choise, your good will to gaine is my wished reward: which shalbe more welcome then Cressus *aboundaunce, and more hartily accepted then any worldly wealth. The last part of this woorke remaineth vnfinished, the which for breuity of time, and speedines in the Imprinting: I was constrained to permit till more limitted leysure. Desiring your Honour to accept this in meane time, as a signe and token of my dutifull goodwill.*

Not long it will be before the rest be finished and the renowned Palmerin *of England with all speede shall be sent you. Thus praying for your prosperitie, and the increase of your Honourable dignitie: I commend your woorthye state to the heauenly eternitie.*

Your Honours moste dutifull
seruaunt at all assayes.
Antony Munday.

To the well disposed Reader.

I MAY be deemed (courteous Reader) more
wanton then wise, and more curious then circumspect: in naming my booke by such a vaine
glorious title, for some will suppose heere are rare
exploytes of martial mindes to be seen: which
when they haue prooued, they finde it to faint.
Othersome will desire for *Venus* daintie dalli-
ances: but *Iuno* dealeth so iustly in this cause, that
their also they misse their marke. Then how (will
some say) can Fame be so furnished: and bothe of
these absent? the matter (say I) shall make manifest what I haue attempted: and then if I be founde
faultie, I will stand to your gentle iudgementes.
That man is very wise that neuer offendeth in
folly, that man is very valiant that neuer meetes
with his match, and that man is very circumspect
that neuer talketh awry, the righteous man offendeth seuen times a day: then needes must the
negligent be found very faulty. It is a good horse
that neuer stumbleth, and he a seuere seruaunt that
neuer displeaseth his maister, then beare with my
rudenesse if I chaunce to offend you: my good
will did labour in hope for to please you.

Againe, some will be inquisitiue, why I am so
willing to welcome *Euphues* into England? he
beeyng so excellent: and my selfe so simple? If
Euphues so wisely dooth wish you beware, and to
preuent the perilles that heedelesse heades may

haue, wishing youth likewise to frame their fancies so fit, that no crooked chaunces doo happen
to harme them: Then like that *Lilly* whose sent is
so sweete, and fauour his freend who wisheth your
welfare. And although my wit be so weake: that I
cannot welcome as I would, and my skyll to simple to gratifye so gentle a gueast: I trust my good
will shall plead me a pardon, and my honest intent be nothing misliked. Thus hoping to
haue your courteous consentes, which is
the reward I cheefest require, I wishe
my woorkes may prooue as profitable
to you in the reading: as they were
delightfull to me in the writing.

Your freend to commaund
A. Munday.

A delicate Disputation gallantlye
discoursed betweene two noble Gentlemen of Italy.

The Argument.

NOT longe since ouer the famous and stupen-
dious Citie of Venice, gouerned Gonzalo
Guicciardo, elected Duke by the most worthye
Orlando Fiorentino. This aforesayde Gonzalo,
(renowmed for his princely gouerment, obayed
for his singuler wisdom, praysed for his pollitique
suppressing of prowde vsurpinge enimies, and
honored for his humilytie to his subiects ingenerall) was not onely accounted as a second Mutio
among his freends and familyars, but euen amonge
his very enemies was also esteemed as a prince
worthy of eternall memory. And nature the more
to agrauate his ioyes in his hoary haires: gaue hym
a Sonne called Zelauto, whose singuler humanitie,
whose puisance in feates of armes, whose dexteri-
tie in witte, and whose comelye shape in personage, caused hym through all Venice to bee greatly
accounted of.

This gallant youth Zelauto (more desirous to
aduaunce his fame by traueilyng straunge countries: then to leade his lyngring life styll in the
court of his famous father) one day by chaunce
tooke courage to open the hidden thoughts which
longe incombred his carefull breast, and hauing

espied his father at such conuenient leasure, as
serued best for his auayle, yeelding his obeysaunce
as dutie beseemed, entred into this discourse.

If (Right woorthy and renowmed Father) nature had adorned me with such rare and excellent
quallities, as might procure an hartes ease and ioy
vnto your princely estate: then would dutie cause
me to keepe my minde in silence, and feare (of
displeasing your aged hart) byd me restrayne my
vowed attempt. But sith I am destitute of that
which my hart desireth, and willing to gaine the
same by painefull industry: I hope I shall purchase
no ill will of your person, nor displease the mindes
of your subiectes in generall. First weigh and consider by your gratious aduisement, that a youthfull minde more desireth the fragrant fieldes: then
the hidden house, Custome confesseth, yea, and
lawe of Nature alloweth, that it is more permanent to a princely courage, to seeke the renowmed
mansion, of the most illustrious and sacred Ladye
Fame: then to drowne his youthfull dayes in gulfs
of gaping greef, in silent sorrows, in vaine
thoughts and cogitations, and also in trifling and
idle exercises, which maketh him more prone vnto
vice then vertue, more apt vnto lewdnes: then
contented liuing, yea, maketh him so friuilous and
fantasticall, that nothing but libidinous thoughtes,
beastly behauiour, is his whole exercise. For then
euery blasing beame, and euery sugred countenaunce of a woman allureth him, that floting on
the Seas of foolish fansie, and hauing abid one
lusty gale of winde, wherewith the Barke of his
body, is beaten against the Rockes of his Ladyes
lookes, then the poore patient falleth into so ex-

treme an extasie, that one worde will kill him, and
an other reuiue him. Thus is he inclosed amid these
subtill snares, while in the warlike feeld he might
enioy his libertie, and their win fame which should
last eternally. These and such like crabbed con-
ceites (deere Father) vrgeth me to craue your
leaue and licence, that I may a while visite straunge
Countries, In which time, I doubt not but to at-
chieue such exploytes, that at my returne it will
be treble ioy to your Princely eares to heare them
recounted.

    Sonne Zelauto (aunswered the Duke) this your
discourse is both commendable, and allowable, for
I lyke well of your intent, and with all my hart
giue consent that for a limitted time you shal seeke
aduentures, which time shall amount vnto .vi.
yeares, and on my blessing I charge thee, not to
breake that appointed time. In the meane while, if
God call me (as my life is vncertaine) I frankly
and freely giue thee all is myne. Wherfore looke
well to thy selfe, that good report may be heard
of thee, which vnto me will be great contentation.
But nowe as touching what ayde and assistance
thou wilt haue with thee: speake, and it shall be
graunted. Good Father (answered Zelauto) none
but onely one to beare me company, which I
know will be sufficient. Well (quoth the Duke)
receiue heere my blessing, this portion of money,
and this knight to beare thee company. And I pray
God in all thy wayes to guide and protect thee,
and so you may depart when you please.

    Zelauto accompanied with his knight, departed
from the Court of his famous Father, and tooke
shipping to goe vnto Naples, from thence, he

trauailled vnto Valentia in Spayne, and chauncing
into the company of certayne English Merchauntes, who in the Latine tongue told him the
happy estate of England, and how a worthy
Princes gouerned their common weale, and all
suche thinges as could not be more praysed then
they deserued. The which Zelauto hearing, craued
of them that he might sayle with them into England, and he woulde liberally reward them. They
beeyng contented, and hauing laden their Shippes
with such necessaryes as they best desyred: within
fewe dayes hoysed sayles, and away they went.

This young youth Zelauto beeyng come into
England, and seene the rare and vertuous vsage of
the illustrious and thrise renowmed Princes, with
the great honour and fauour which he obtayned
among her woorthy Lordes: purposed to stay still
there. But yet remembring, that although he sawe
one place: many others were as yet vnseene, after
a yeere expyred, he tooke shipping into Persia,
and so departed. In processe of time he had visited
many straunge Countryes, sustayned many and
wonderfull iniuryes among the Turkes, which
after shall be declared. And returning homeward,
happened on the borders of Sicile, where Fortune
was fauourable vnto him: that vnawares he happened on the caue of a valiaunt Knight, who was
a Christian, and hauing committed an hainous offence: fled out of his owne Countrie, and inhabited there in a silent Cell, among the woods. This
Knight beyng named Astræpho, and hearing the
trampling of one about his denne: tooke his weapons, and came foorth. He beeing greatly abashed
at the sight of Zelauto, for that in tenne yeeres
space he neither sawe man nor woman: but had

lyued there a sauage lyfe: forgetting all poyntes of
humanitie sayd. What varlet, art thou come to
seeke my death? thou art welcome, and therewith all strooke at Zelauto, who alas through
tediousnesse of trauell, and long beeyng
without any sustenaunce: was constrayned to yeeld, and falling on his
knees submitted himselfe to his
mercye, which Astræpho seeing,
sayd as hereafter followeth.

¶ *The Fountayne of Fame, distylling*
his dainty drops, in an Orchard of Amarous Aduentures.

☙ Astræpho, *hauing conquered* Zelauto, *sayth.*

WHAT so sodayne and straunge Metamorphesis is this? Art thou a Knight, that professest thy selfe a Souldier vnder God *Mars* his Ensigne: and so soone conquered? What doost thou think that this thy submission, shall hinder me of my pretended purpose? Thy death it is I seeke, and more honour shall I obtaine by the slaughter of such a wretche: then to let thee lyue any longer time.

Zelauto.

Most woorthy syr, if euer any iot of clemency consysted in your valiant brest: then respect I craue, the distressed case of your poore vassaill. And meruayll not though in force I am not able to resist against you, for that the great miseries which I haue susteyned in these my tedious trauayles, hath quite bereued me of my manly might.

Astræpho.

The Lyon dooth easily conquer his yeelding pray.

A bad excuse (say they) is better then none at all, you pleade nowe simplicitie, through the defect of your valiancie, and by such sophisticall

Sillogismes, to beguile me craftilie, no, no, poore wretch, harde was thy hap to light in his handes: who seeketh the subuertion of thy state, and to cause thee yeelde thy neck to the rigor of his manly might. Long delayes neede not, differ not with dalliance, for I am bent to thy vtter ruin.

Zelauto.

Small hope hath the siely Lambe, in the rauening iawes of the greedy Woolfe, to escape with life, lyttle comfort hath the pensiue prisoner at the poynt of death, to shun so harde a lot. So I (poore soule) in the handes of a Tirant (who more regardeth blood, then bountie, more respecteth death then delyuerie, and more vaunteth of villainy, then any valiancie) what succour can I haue in this my sorrowe? what hope in this my so harde hap, to craue life it auayleth not, to desire a respit it booteth not, and to striue against the streame, were but a presuming boldnes, if I wish for death I gayne it, if I wish for life, I lose it. What shall betide thee poore distressed *Zelauto?* hap weale or woe, hap life or death, hap blisse or bale: I will aduenture by fayre woords to intreate him, and so it may happen to stay his rigor. Good syr, if euer humanitie harbored in that noble brest, or if euer pittie pronounced her puissaunce on your princely person: then respect (I pray) the disstressed case of your conquered captiue. Small honour shall you haue by my death, and no Fame to vaunt on a naked man. My life can lyttle pleasure you, and my death lesse, therefore seeke not to shed his blood, who at your will and pleasure voweth bothe heart and hand at your courteous commaundement.

Where as Fortune is so aduerse, small hope is to be had.

Zelauto at last by faire woordes, dooth seeke to win fauour.

Astræpho.

In deed I confesse, that small honor is his due that vaunts on so prostrate a pray, and therefore somewhat hath thy woords satisfied my former desire, for in deed, a straunge and wonderfull sight it is to me, to see a man that haue seene none these ten yeeres passed, therefore pardon what is spoken, there resteth the greater amendes to be made.

Zelauto.

Syr, more bound vnto you in duty, then euer I am able to performe: I yeeld you all thankes possible that resteth in so poore a person, and I doubt not but that God hath appoynted all at the best, for these fiue yeeres and more haue I visited straunge countreyes: and neuer yet did I happen on any such aduenture.

Astræpho.

And haue you ben a Traueiler syr? then vnfolde I pray you what hath bene the mishaps, that the frowning Fates vnto you hath alotted, and first tell I pray you, of what soyle, what Parentage and kindred you are of, and what is your name.

Zelauto.

Syr, as necessitie hath no lawe, so neede at this present vrgeth me to speake. In this your Caue (I am sure) you are not destitute of victualls, the which I want, wherfore if it shall please you, to refresh his hunger, who is ready to faynt: I will discourse vnto you afterward my whole aduentures at large.

Astræpho.

Alas syr, if such simple fare as I haue may seeme to suffise your hunger: come neere, and we will goe to dinner, and afterward will we discourse of such matters as (perchaunce) may be profitable to bothe.

Zelauto.

With right good will syr, and a thousand thanks for your courtesie, extended vnto me in this my vnlooked for mishap. And it may so fortune, that after our conference had together: we may with our pleasaunt talke well content eche other.

Astræpho.

Well syr, approche this my homely Mansion, and I desire you to accept the goodwill of your poore hoste.

❦ Astræpho *and* Zelauto *goeth to* dinner, and their talke after they had well refreshed themselues.

Astræpho.

NOW Syr, how lyke you of your homely en-tertaynment? where no better is, bad may suffise, and to a contented minde nothing is preiu-diciall. You see howe poore folkes are content with pottage, Ritch men may goe to dynner when they wyll, and poore men when they may.

Honest talk passeth away the time pleas-auntly.

Zelauto.

A freendlie gratula-
tion for curtesie
receyued.

Syr, he that wyll looke a giuen Horse in the mouth: is vnwoorthy of the gyft, your fare hath suffised me, and you haue vanquisht him, who would haue murdred mee. What dayntie delycates is to be looked for in desert places? it suffiseth the Courts of Princes to haue their delycate fare, and to poore Trauellers, the homeliest dyshe is welcome, they looke for no after seruice, and in steede

Ne ob diuitias
laudaris virum in-
dignum.

of sauce, they vse their hungrie appetite, we syt not to haue our Table taken vp, we chop at noone, and chew it soone. They in their superfluitie, we in our want. They in their prodigalitie, we spare for an after extremitie. Who more couetous then they, that haue all at their pleasure? and who more freendly then they, that haue a lyttle, and impart thereof to their freendes. They spend, we spare, they vse excesse, and we hardnesse. And therefore sayth *Tullie:*

Cicero in partitioni-
bus Orat.

We ought to haue great respect,
least that the hydden vice:
That dooth vppon the vertues tende,
dooth slylie vs intyce.

Cato Senior.

.The elder *Cato* also vppon this sayth.

By two thinges I encrease my wealth,
by tylling of my ground:
The other by good husbandrie,
that I therein haue found.
For why, the one aboundaunce bringes,
as much as heart can chuse:
The other dooth me wisely teach,
howe I the same should vse.

Thus syr may you see howe sparing is commended: and now somwhat wyll I speake as concerning inordinate spending, and laciuious excesse, which hath the personnes that vsed it, greatly
abused.

Lucullus, for his sumptuous buyldings, and his
inordinate expences, thought among the *Romaines*
to be magnified, for that he thought to excell all
his predecessors. But *Pompey* hearing thereof, and
greatly desirous to see if all were as the common
brute dyd blase it abroade: iorneyed vntyll he
came vnto *Lucullus* Mansion place, where seeing
that the thing it selfe excelled the common report,
in derision sayde vnto *Lucullus*.

> *These gay and gorgious buyldings heere,*
> *be set with Stories braue:*
> *And open windowes, that the ayre,*
> *free entraunce in may haue.*
> *For Summer they delightfull are,*
> *and gallant to beholde:*
> *But when that* Hiems *dooth approche,*
> *her blastes wyll make you colde.*

Truly, in my opinion, his woordes stoode with
great reason, and ought also greatly to be esteemed
of, for fancie is so fickle, that each tryfling toy
(though it be not profitable, if it be pleasaunt) is
now a dayes most desired. As *Lucullus*, he was all
in his prodigallitie, but nothing regarded in the
ende the myserie. Farther we reade, how *Apollos*
sonne *Æsculapius*, for his prodigall minde, and
vnsatiable desire of rytches: was cast into the bot-
tomles *Limbo*, among the Fiendes, and Diuels of
hell. And diuers other (which were too tedious to
rehearse) which got their goods wickedly, and

Lucullus.

Pompey.

*An excellent priuie
nyp giuen vnto* Lu-
cullus.

Aesculapius *sonne to*
Apollo.

spent it laciuiously. And therefore I wyll say with *Tullie*.

Tullie.

Malè parta, malè dilabuntur.

Zelauto *dooth re-*
turne to giue his
freend thankes for his
lyberalyty.

But now Sir, returning to our contented feast passed, for my part, I am to yeelde a thousand thankes, and to shewe you the like curtesie if I come in place where abilitie shall serue me, And wish you not to thinke, but as it was lyberally and curteously bestowed: so was it gratefully and hartily accepted. And now may I well say, that he which neuer tasteth necessitie: knoweth not what want is. For whyles I tasted on our Courtly iunckets, I neuer thought I should haue bene driuen so neere, but now, this state contenteth me farre better then my former, which was nothing but vanitie.

Neede hath no law,
necessitie breaketh
stone Walles.

Astræpho.

A promise made, may
alwayes be claymed
for a due debt.

Syr, this your pleasaunt discourse, is bothe pithy and profitable, and sauoureth of the sence which prooueth perfect in the conclusion. But now as touching our talke before dinner, I must not forget your promise, for that you sayd, I should vnderstand the sum of your myseries, your aduentures happened in trauayle, your name, Countrey, and parentage, which tolde: I shall declare the better some of my straunge aduentures.

Zelauto.

Zelauto *accordeth to*
his freendly request.

Indeede syr, promise is due debt we say, and according to promise, I will vnfolde that which is bothe straunge, and lamentable, wherefore giue me leaue I desire you, and you shall heare, the perillous Pylgrimage which I poore soule haue passed.

Fyrst syr, as concerning my Countrey, Parentage and name: I giue you to vnderstand, that I am sonne to the woorthy *Gonzalo Guiciardo*, who is Duke of *Venice*, and by name I hight *Zelauto*. Long tyme had I soiourned in the Court of my noble Father, not knowing the vse and order of forreigne Countreyes, wherevnto my minde was adicted, wherfore at the last, I ventured boldly, and tolde my Father what in heart I had attempted: the which he well lyking of: gaue his consent, and so I and an other Knight (whome my Father gaue me for companion) traueyled towarde *Naples*, and in our trauayle: we met with certaine Outlawes, whom we call *Banditie*.

.These cruell fellowes set vppon mee, wounded mee verie sore, slew my Companion, dispoyled me of my apparell and money, leauing mee for dead. But God more mercifull then these Villaines were tyrannicall, would not suffer mee to perish in their handes, but (they beeing gone) gaue mee the power to creepe on all fowre to *Naples*. When I was come thyther: I knew not what to doo, because I was freendlesse, moneylesse, and dispoyled out of my Garmentes. At last, hauing espyed an *Osteria:* I boldly entered, putting my selfe in the handes of God, to whome I referred the paying of my charges.

Zelauto telleth his first trauayles.
Gonzalo Guiciardo, *Duke of* Venice.

His trauelling to Naples. Banditie, *called Outlawes, doo wound* Zelauto.

His hard escaping to Naples.

His bolde entraunce into an Inne.

¶ *Heere* Zelauto *telleth what happened*
to him in the Osteria, and what freendshippe he found with
Madonna Vrsula, Madonna della Casa.

Madonna Vrsula,
*the Mistresse of the
house.*

*Her freendly enter-
tainment.*

Margarita la doni-
zela.

*A freendly and gen-
tle offer.*

Madonna Vrsula
*her returne to Ze-
lauto.*

BEING come to this *Osteria*, I entered, and the
first person that I sawe, was the Misteresse of
the house, who was named *Madonna Vrsula*, a
very proper, pleasaunt, kinde and courteous Gentlewoman. At my comming in, you are welcome
Gentleman (quoth she). Is it your will I pray you
to haue lodging? I answered, yea surely, vntill
such time as my wounds be healed, and my selfe
better refreshed. With that quoth she to one of her
maydens. *Margarita*, conduct this Gentleman to
the best Chamber, make him a good fire, and carry
vp with you a Boccall of winne and a manchet, in
the meane while, wil I make ready his supper. And
Gentleman (quoth she) what thing so euer it be
that you want: call for, and if it be to be gotten
in *Naples* for loue or money, you shall haue it.
Heere was yet good entertainment, after so hard
mishaps, my greefe and sorrowe was not so great
before, for the losse of my companion, my money
and apparail: but her cheerefull woordes did as
much reuiue my hart. And so yeelding her great
thankes I went vp into my Chamber, where
against my comming, I found a very great fire, my
Chaire ready set for me to sit downe with my
Cushion, and my boots pulled of, warme Pantofles brought vnto me, and a cleane kertcher put on
my head. So hauing sitten there about the space of
halfe an houre: vp came the misteris of the house,
who taking a glasse, filled it with Wine, and came
vnto me saying. Sir (*Per licentia vostra*) I salute

you. So causing an other glasse to be filled with wine: shee gaue it me, whom I pledged as courteously as I could. Then tooke she an other Chaire, and sat downe by me, commaunding her mayden seruaunt (who attended there) to giue place, who making courtesie to me and her misteris, departed. Then began she to talke with me in this order as followeth.

An Italian courtesie.

She commaundeth her maide to depart, and beginneth her talke.

◁ The talke that the Misteris of the house had with Zelauto.

GENTLEMAN, as I very well esteeme of your courteous and ciuill demeanour: so am I desirous to knowe of whence you are, and what misfortunes hath happened vnto you, that you are so greeuously wounded. Pardon me I pray you, if I demaund the thing which you are not willing to vtter, and also because on so suddaine acquaintaunce, I enterprise to question with you. Gentlewoman (quoth I) the good opinion, and great liking that you haue of me, is as yet vndeserued, and as yet you haue seene no such ciuilitie in me as deserueth to be commended. But yet I am to yeeld you thanks for your good liking. And as touching my mishaps, and this straunge aduenture which hath happened, and if you please to attend the discourse: I will tell you all. I am of *Padua*, and there my parentes dwell, and beeing minded to see the vse of other Countries: I left my Parents, beeing well stored with money, and a Gentleman also which bare me company.

Madonna Vrsula her talke.

Zelauto his reply.

A fayned excuse to collour the matter.

Beeing come heere into the kingdome: among the woods we encountred with certaine *Banditie*, who set vpon vs, slew my companion, left me for dead, and spoyled me of all my money and apparell. So God helping me: I haue hardly got hether with my life.

Thus haue you knowen some part of my mishaps, nowe consider thereof by your good construction. Sir (quoth shee) your hap hath been hard, and little doo your Parentes knowe of this your suddaine aduersitie. Be not discouraged therfore, heere shall you abide vntill such time as your woundes are healed, and that you haue perfectly recouered your health, and beside what money you want: you shalbe well prouided therof. Therefore let not this mishap dismay you, a freend in necessitie: is better then a hundred in prosperitie. But are you not acquainted with any here in *Naples?* Yes (quoth I) I haue letters to *Signor Giouanni Martino*, from my Father, for the recouerie of money, as now I stand in need thereof.

Well Sir (quoth she) pardon my boldnes I pray you, and first trie your freend, and if he faile: you know where to speede of mony, and of a greater matter if neede require, In the meane time, I will see how neere your supper is ready, and wil come againe and beare you company. How like you now Sir of the freendly entertainment that I obtayned at this Gentlewomans hand, and also of her proffered courtesie?

Astræpho.

Certainly *Zelauto*, you are much bound vnto that Gentlewoman, for in my opinion, you might haue gone to twentie *Osteriaes* in *Naples* and not

Her encouragement giuen a freshe to Zelauto.

Signor Giouanni Martino, *a merchaunt in* Naples.

Madonna Vrsula *her courteous promise.*

Astræpho *telleth his iudgement on this matter.*

haue founde the like freendship. But proceede I pray you, how sped you with your freend for your money, and how did your hostes deale with you?

Zelauto.

You shall heare Sir. After she was departed out of the Chamber, there came vp two modest Damsels, and they couered the table. At last came she vp againe. Sir (quoth she) doo you not thinke it long before you goe to supper? No (quoth I) in good time yet, you neede not make such hast. Well Sir (quoth she) anon heere will a Surgion come, who shall dresse your woundes, and looke vnto you till you be perfectly healed.

Zelauto proceedeth in his discourse. She returneth demaunding if he wil go to supper.

Then was our Supper brought vp very orderly, and she brought me water to washe my handes. And after I had washed I sat downe, and she also, but concerning what good cheere we had: I neede not make report. For all thinges was in as good order, and aswell to my contentation: as euer it was in my Fathers Court.

They goe to supper.

After Supper (quoth she) Sir but that you are so ouercharged with trauell, and faynt with your woundes I would play a game or two with you at the *Primero*. But we will referre that till to morrowe at night. Then came in the Chirurgion and he dressed my woundes, and water was brought to wash my feete, my Bed was warmed, and so I went and layde me downe to take my rest.

She proffereth to play with Zelauto.

A Chirurgion commeth and dresseth his woundes.

¶ *In the morning* Zelauto *sendeth*

for Signor Giouani Martino, *of whom he should receiue money, and how he sped, and of his farder freendship that he had with* Madonna Vrsula.

In the morning Ma-
donna Vrsula *com-
meth to see* Zelauto.

NOWE when I had well and sufficiently re-
posed my selfe all night, and in the morning
finding my selfe more strong and forceable, then
before I was: I thought to haue risen, But vp came
Misteris *Vrsula* agayne, and comming to my Bed
side, she sayd. Gentleman, haue you taken quiet
rest this night or no? Yes surely Misteris (quoth I)
I neuer slept so soundly in all my life before, and
credit me, I finde my selfe very well amended.
Wherefore now I will rise. No not yet Sir (quoth
she) you shall first make your Collation in bed,

*They fall in talke
againe.*

with such things as I haue ordayned, and haue
your wounds dressed agayne: and then shall you
rise. I thanke you good Misteris *Vrsula* (quoth I)
and surely it seemeth very straunge vnto me, that
on a straunger you should bestowe such courtesie?
Sir (quoth she) on the vertuous and well disposed,
no one can bestowe courtesie sufficient. As for my
part, to such Gentlemen, as vpon some occasion
are fallen into want and necessitie: I thinke it a
great poynt of humanitie, to bestowe on them

Lactantius de vero
cultu. Chap. *12*.

freendly hospitalitie. And therefore I followe the
minde of *Lactantius*, who sayth, there is a kinde of
hospitalitie, which is vsed for a priuate gayne and
secret commoditie, and for no loue fauour nor

*Inholders and Tauer-
ners for commoditie.*

freendship at all. Of which sort I am none, I referre that to common Inholders, and those tipling

Tauerners. Let them entertayne for their commoditie, and I for courtesie. I remember how *Cæsar* dooth commend in his Commentaries, the great
fauour and freendship that the *Germaines* shewed
to straungers. For not only would they defend
them from their enemies: but also entertaine them
with meate, drinke, clothing and lodging. The
Scripture also maketh mention, how *Abraham*, receiued into his house (as he thought) men, but he
receiued God himselfe. *Lot* also receiued Angels
in the shape of men into his house. Wherefore for
his hospitalitie *Lot* escaped the fire of *Sodom* and
Gomorra. *Rahab*, for the same likewise, with all
hers was preserued from the terror of death.

And what saith Saint *Ambrose?* Who can tell if
we welcome *Christe* or no, when we giue freendly
entertainment to straungers? Therfore sir seeme
not to be offended I pray you, though I preach on
this fashion, for both loue, dutie, faith and charity,
dooth bind me to welcome you hether curteously.
Alas good Misteris (quoth I) I see well your great
curtesie, but I knowe not how to requite the same.
Sir (quoth she) what you are not able to doo:
God will doo for you, and it is sufficient for me to
receiue thankes at your handes, for greater is my
reward in heauen. And with that she departed to
fetch me my breakefast. Now syr, tell me I pray
you, if the memory of this rare and vertuous
woman is not woorthy to be rehearsed?

Astræpho.

Now credit me *Zelauto*, she surpasseth all that
euer I heard of, both for promptnes of wit, vertue
of the minde, and excellencie in qualities. But I

*Cæsar in his Com-
mentaries commend-
eth the Germaines.*

Abraham. Genesis.

*Sodom and
Gomorra.*

*Rahab deliuered from
death for the same.*

*S. Ambrose as touch-
ing the entertainment
of straungers.*

*Zelauto answereth
her learned discourse.*

*Astræpho vnfoldeth
his iudgement
agayne.*

pray you could she repeat these Authors whereof you haue showen, so readily?

Zelauto.

Yea Sir, and a great many more, which I am not able to rehearse. For surely the rare excellencie that I did beholde in her: made me so amazed, that I coulde not attend all her discourses.

Astræpho.

Astræpho *desireth to heare more of this matter.*

Now for Gods sake proceede, and let me heare more of this: for surely shee is woorthy of eternall remembraunce, in my iudgement.

Zelauto.

Zelauto *now goeth to breake fast.*

Then came vp two Damsels, the one brought a pretie litle table couered, and set it on the Beds side, and the other brought such necessaries as did belong to that we went about. Then came she her selfe, and brought me such meate, as I neuer did eate the like before: and what other cheere was there I referre that to your iudgement. But then quoth she to one of her Damsels. Goe and fetch me my Lute, and I will recreat this Gentleman with a pleasant song, the copie whereof she gaue me, and for a neede I could rehearse it.

She sendeth for her Lute.

Astræpho.

Astræpho *desireth to heare her song.*

Nowe good *Zelauto* let me heare it, for I am sure it is woorthy the rehearsall.

Zelauto.

Since you are so desirous: you shall, wherefore attend it diligently.

¶ *The Song which misteris* Vrsula
sung to her Lute, to Zelauto.

As Loue is cause of ioy,
    So Loue procureth care:
As Loue dooth end annoy,
    So Loue dooth cause despaire.
But yet I oft heard say,
    and wise men like did giue:
That no one at this day,
    without a loue can liue.
  And thinke you I, will loue defie:
  No, no, I loue, vntill I die.

Zelauto *reherseth it.*

Loue knits the sacred knot,
    Loue hart and hand dooth binde:
Loue will not shrinke one iot,
    but Loue dooth keepe his kinde.
Loue maketh freendes of foes,
    loue stayes the common wealth:
Loue dooth exile all woes,
    that would impaire our health.
  Since loue dooth men and monsters mooue:
  What man so fond will loue disprooue?

Loue keepes the happy peace,
    Loue dooth all strife alay:
Loue sendeth rich increase,
    Loue keepeth warres away.
Loue of it selfe is all,
    Loue hath no fellowe mate:
Loue causeth me, and shall,
    Loue those, that loue my state.

Then loue will I, vntill I dye:
And all fond Loue I will defye.

FINIS.

Zelauto.

How like you now Sir of her Song? is it not
bothe pithie and excellent, dooth it not beare a
singuler and great vnderstanding withall?

Astræpho.

Astræpho *amased at*
her singularity
knoweth not what to
say.

If I should speake all I thinke, you would hardly
beleeue me, for surely, her song contayneth great
and learned poyntes of wisedome, and requireth
a more expert and learned heade then mine to define thereon: And certainely it amazeth me to
heare that such excellencie should remayne in a
woman. But I pray you proceede, and let me heare
more of this matter?

Zelauto.

Zelauto *goeth on*
with his tale.

After she had ended her song: Quoth she, Gentleman I trust you are not ignoraunt of the meaning of my Song, for perhaps you might alleadge
some poynts of lewdnes or lightnes, that a woman
should so much commend Loue, but my intent
therefore I referre to your good construction.
And nowe sir since you haue refreshed your selfe:

The Chirurgion com-
meth and dresseth
him againe.

let the Chirurgion vse his cunning to your
woundes: and in the meane while, I will send for
Signor Giouanni Martino, and then we shall see
what he will say to you. I thanke you good Misteris *Vrsula* (quoth I) and I pray you let him be
sent for.

The comming in of
Signor Giouanni
Martino.

So after that the Chirurgion had dressed me and
was departed: in came *Signor Giouanni Martino.*

Who seeing mee, kneeled downe and kissed my hand, the which *Madonna Vrsula*, marueiled at. Then quoth I to him in his eare, I pray doo not vse any such curtesie whereby I may be knowen, for because I would not be knowen to any, but if they demaund of you who I am: say that I am of *Padua*. Well syr (quoth he) your minde shalbe fulfilled in all thinges.

Then I gaue him Letters, which when he had read: he departed and brought me seuen hundred Crownes, saying, spende these whyles you are heere, and at your departure you shall haue more.

Then spake *Madonna Vrsula* to him. Syr, doo you knowe this Gentleman. Yea forsoothe (quoth he) his Parents are of great credit in *Padua*, wherfore I pray you let him want nothing. Well syr (quoth she) he hath wanted nothing yet, nor shall not, if you had not spoken. But nowe dynner is ready, and I will desire you to beare him company: Yes (quoth he) that I shall, wyllingly.

Well syr, to be short, there had I passed ten or twelue dayes, and was perfect whole, and then I would needes depart. Which when she saw, she was verie sorie and pensiue. But yet (quoth she) although Syr you doo depart: I hope if it be your Fortune to iourney this way againe homewarde, you wyll take vp your homely lodging heere. And in token that you shall remember mee: take heere this Iewell, and weare it I desyre you for my sake.

Zelauto *woulde needes depart from his hostes. Her sorow for his departure.*

I yeelded her a thousand thankes, recompenced her seruauntes, payed my charges. So on the morrowe morning I departed, accompanied with a Gentleman, who was an especiall freende vnto *Signor Giouanni Martino*. And thus haue you heard the whole discourse of my first trauayle.

Zelauto *departeth from* Naples.

Astræpho.

Surely heere hath beene a gallant discourse, and
worthy the memorie, you are much bound in
curtesie vnto that Gentlewoman. And I would it
were my fortune once to happen on such an
hostes. But whether iourneyed you then from
Naples?

Zelauto.

Zelauto *commeth to* Valentia *in* Spaine, *and trauayleth with Gentlemen to* Ciuill, *from thence to* Lysbone, *where he happeneth on certaine Englyshe Merchants with whom he talketh as concerning their Countrey.*

Sir (as I was about to tell you) in fewe dayes I
ariued at *Valentia* in *Spayne,* where it was my
chaunce to meete with certaine Gentlemen, who
trauailed vnto *Ciuill,* and with them I went, there
I remayned and my companion three dayes. From
thence I went to *Lysbone,* where as I lodged in
the house of one *Pedro de Barlamonte.* There
lodged also certayne English Merchauntes, whom
I beeing very willing to talke with all: one night
desired them to take part of a Supper with me.
They spake the Latin tongue very well, and so of
them I questioned about the vsage of their Countrey, and that of long time I had heard great commendation thereof: Also of a mayden Queene
that swayed the Scepter there. I asked them

Their answer.

whether it was so or no? They answered it was,
and gaue me to vnderstand so much of their Coun-

Zelauto *goeth with the Merchants to* S. Lucas, *so towards* England.

trey: that I would needs, goe with them into England, who in deede were very willing, and so they
hauing ended their Merchandize: we iourneyed to
S. Lucas, and within fewe dayes I tooke shipping
into the so famous bruted Realme of England.

¶ *Heere* Zelauto *telleth how with*
certayne English Merchauntes he sayled into England,
and what happened vnto him.

Astræpho.

W hy then you stayed but a while in *Spayne.*

Zelauto.

No sure, for after I and my Companion had
heard of the fame of Englande: we could not set-
tle our mindes to staye there, but thought euery
day a yeere vntill we myght come into England.

Astræpho.

And is England so famous? I pray you declare
vnto mee what you haue seene there that deserued
so great commendations.

Astræpho *requyreth
to know of* England.

Zelauto.

That I shall, wherefore I desire you to giue eare
vnto this discourse, for it is both straunge and excellent.

After as we were departed from the coast of
Spayne, in a three weekes space we ariued vpon
the coast of England, and landed at a certaine
hauen that in their language they call *Douer,* the
maister and his mate, with two or three other of
the ship bare vs company into the towne, where
we came to an Inne (as they call them) and beeing
set downe, one of them called for drinke, which
was such as I did neuer see the lyke before, for
they call it Beere, and such a language they speake,
as is bothe straunge and wonderfull, for I knowe

Zelauto *came into*
England *and landeth
at* Douer.

He drincketh English
Beere, and merueyleth
at the Language.

not to what I should best liken it. Well sayd I to my companion, now we are heere, what shall we doo? We knowe not what they say, nor they can not vnderstande vs, I thinke it were best to hyre some of these that are in the ship which speake the Latin tongue to conduct vs vntill we come to some of our Countrymen, wherof they tolde vs was a great many there. He was verye well contented, and so I desired the maister that wee might haue one of his men to guyde vs, who in deede verye courteously consented.

Zelauto craueth of the maister for a guide.

And then he sent to his Shyp for one *Roberto*, a verie merry and pleasaunt fellowe, and he spake our language very well, he gaue him very great charge, that he should vse vs well, vntyll we came to their cheefe Cittie, which they call *London*, and then as soone as we came thyther: to bring vs to some of our countreymen. So we contented the Maister, got vp on Horsebacke, and so rode to *London*.

Roberto a very mery fellow appointed for a guide to Zelauto.

֍ Zelauto *and his companion being*
come to London, *through the meanes of* Roberto *their
guyde, they are brought to the house of one* Signor
Giulio di Pescara, *who entertained them very
curteously.*

O VR mery Companion, hauing brought vs to *London:* shewed vs many fayre and comly syghtes, as first he had vs into their *Bursse*, where abooue were so many fine Shops full of braue

Zelauto is come to London to the Royall Exchaunge.

deuises, and euery body sayd, a mad term that they had, *What lack ye, what lack ye.* I merueyled what they meant by it, then I asked *Roberto* what they sayd. So he tolde me, that they asked me what I would buye, if I would haue any of their fine wares. And surely in that place were many very proper and comely Women: Then he had vs, and shewed vs a very fine Vaute vnder the same, where there was a great many Shops lyke-wise. So then it began to waxe somthing toward the euening, and then he conducted vs to the house of one *Signor Giulio*, a Gentleman of *Pescara*, where we had very gallant entertaynement, and so well esteemed of, as if we had bene in our owne Countrey. This *Giulio* had maried an English Woman, who in deede, was so gentle of nature, so comely in qualities, and so proper in personage, that sure mee thought she excelled. Of her lyke-wise we were very gently welcommed, and a very gallant Chamber prepared, with all things so neces-sary, and seruaunts to attend on vs so dilligently, that sure it was not in vaine that *England* had such excellent commendation. My Companion sayd, he was neuer so quiet, and so well at his hearts ease: as he was there, beeing but so lyttle tyme there. For in deede (to say the trueth) I wanted nothing, but euerie thing was ready at halfe a woordes speaking, and with great reuerence also.

To the house of this aforesayd *Signor Giulio*, resorted diuers Gentlemen, which were of the Court of England, who shewed vs such courtesie, as it is vnspeakable. But all this whyle I would not be knowen what I was, but told them that I was a Gentleman of *Naples*, and my name was *Zelauto*, and that I came for my pleasure to see the Coun-

Zelauto is brought to Signor Giulio di Pescara, *of his Coun-trey.*

Zelauto lyketh well of the seruyce in England.

Zelauto commeth acquainted with Gentlemen of the Englishe Court.

trey. These Gentlemen, some of them dyd pertayne to men of great Honour, in the sayd Court, whome I lykewise came acquainted with all. But to recount the rare and excellent modestie, the vertuous lyfe adorned with ciuilytie, the hautie courage and Martiall magnanimitie, and their singuler qualyties in generall, though I had the gallantest memorie in the world, the pregnantest wit, and the rarest eloquence to depaynt them: I know my selfe were vnable to doo it.

He chaunceth to see the noble Queene *of* England.

It was my chaunce within a whyle after I was acquaynted with those woorthy Lordes of Honour: to come in presence where theyr vertuous Mayden *Queene* was. But credit mee, her heauenly hew, her Princely personage, her rare Sobrietie, her singuler Wisedome: made mee stand as one bereft of his sences. For why, before mine eyes I sawe one that excelled, all the woorthy Dames that euer I haue read of.

Astræpho.

But stay *Zelauto*, dyd you see that peerelesse Paragon? and is she so rare and excellent as you make her to be?

Zelauto.

Oh Syr, neuer can my tongue giue halfe a quarter of the prayse, that is due to that rare *Arabian Phœnix.* Were *Mars* himself alyue: he would stand agast at her Heauenly behauior. And as *Timantes*, when he drew the mournfull portrait, of King *Agamemnon*, for the losse of his Daughter, could not set foorth his face correspondent to the sorrow that is conteyned: left the same couered with a vayle to the iudgement of others. So I, because

Timantes.

Agamemnon.

I am vnable to paynt foorth her passing prayse, according as desert deserueth: I remyt her vnder the vayle of Eternall memorie, to the graue iudgement of others.

Astræpho.

What now *Zelauto?* why, the Goddesses and the Graces them selues, coulde but deserue this commendation, and I am sure she is none.

Zelauto.

Were it possyble for a Goddesse to remayne on the earth at this day: credit mee, it were shee. For thus much I wyll tell yee. It is not to all Countreyes vnknowen, how well her Grace dooth vnderstand and speake the languages, that of her selfe without any interpretour: she is able to aunswer any Ambassadour, that commeth to her Maiestie. Also, it is not vnknowen, howe her Princely Maiestie made the minde of the valiant *Marques Vitelli* (Ambassador sent from the King of *Spayne*) to be marueylously mooued. This *Vitelli*, hath bene knowen a excellent warriour, and yet the rare excellencie of this *Queene* had almost put him cleane out of conceyt. That as he sayde him selfe: he was neuer so out of countenaunce before any Prince in all his lyfe.

Marques Vitelli, Ambassador of Spayne.

It is in vaine of the *Grecians* to vaunt of their *Sappho, Corinna, Eriune, Praxilla, Telesilla, Cleobulina,* nor yet the *Pithegoreans* brag of theyr *Diotima,* and *Aspasia,* for theyr lyues, this is she that excelleth them all: and therfore will I say.

Sappho, Corinna, Eriune, Praxilla, Telesilla, Cleobulina, Pithogareans, Diotima, *and* Aspasia.

O decus Anglorum virgo clarissima viuas:
Donec terrigenis Præbebit lumina Titan.

O Virgin Queene, the rarest gem,
loue graunt thy happy race:
That whyle Dan Titan giues his lyght,
Thou mayst enioy thy place.

Titan.

Let all true English harts, pronounce whyle they haue breath:
God saue and prosper in renown, our Queene Elyzabeth.
Viuat, vincat, regnat, Elyzabetha.

Astræpho.

Zelauto, these your woordes dooth agrauate an exceeding ioye in my minde, and causeth mee to thyrst with *Tantalus*, vntyll it be my Fortune to see that happy Land, that thryse happy Princes, whome if she be as you make report, would cause bothe men and monsters to adore. But I pray you Syr proceede, and let me heare what happened vnto you in that Countrey?

Tantalus.

Zelauto.

Syr, after I had stayed there a whyle (to show this gallant Princes pastime) certaine of her woorthy and famous Lordes assembled in a Tournament, the brauest sight that euer I saw, and with this gallant troupe, there came a Pageant as they call them, wherein were men that spake all Languages. O syr, I am not able to speake sufficient in prayse thereof.

The Pageant with all languages before the Queen.

The Pageant with Apollo, and the nine Muses.

At an other time, there was a braue and excellent deuise which went on wheeles without the helpe of any man. Therein sate *Apollo*, with his heauenly crew of Musique. Beside a number of straunge deuises, which are out of my remembraunce.

But yet I remember one thing more, which was a braue and comely Shippe, brought in before her Maiestie, wherin were certaine of her noble Lordes, and this Ship was made with a gallant deuise, that in her presence it ran vpon a Rock, and was dispoyled. This credit me was the very brauest deuise that euer I sawe, and woorthy of innumerable commendations.

The Ship before her Maiestie.

Astræpho.

Oh admirable Princes, whose singuler vertues, mooues the mindes of such noble Personages, by dayly deedes to demonstrate, and by vsual actions to acquaint her Princely estate with such myraculous motions, as you *Zelauto* make report of.

Astræpho *falleth into admiration with him selfe.*

Zelauto.

If I were able to rehearse all that I haue seene: then I know you could not chuse but say your selfe, that she is well woorthy of farre greater, if possible there might be such: as for example these thinges I haue tolde you, which are yet in my remembraunce may make the matter manifest, bothe the Pageants, and also this seemely Shyp wherof I haue spoken.

Astræpho.

Why? is there any Prince that can wishe or desire to lyue in more worldly pleasure, then that famous and illustrious Queene? Or can there be more vertues resident in an earthly Creature, then her noble lyfe maketh so ample mencion of? Surely in my opinion it were vnpossible: for credit me, the rare rule of her vertuous life: maketh her Land and People in such happy estate. Wherfore

The admiration of Astræpho *at the passed tale of* Zelauto.

good *Zelauto*, conceale not any of this matter from me, for surely I think my self happy to come to the hearing therof.

Zelauto.

Astræphos *earnest request, compelleth* Zelauto *to proceede to deeper matters.*

Since syr, you seeme so importune on me, and that my homly Tales doo so much delyght you: giue eare, and I wyll reade you heere one of the rarest deuises that euer you heard of. Which was a comely sort of Courtiers, prepared in a Tournament to recreate the minde of their Princes and Souereigne.

Astræpho.

Where want of sufficiencie remayneth, to counteruayle your euer approued courtesie: accept in token therof alwayes at your commaundement my dutifull seruice and loyaltie, and attendaunce shall not want, tyll I haue heard these discourses.

☙ Zelauto *taketh out of his Scrip*
a Book, wherin he readeth a gallant deuise presented in a Tournament, which he sawe in England.

Zelauto *to pleasure his freend, telleth him an excellent and braue deuise doone in* England.

FIRST syr, to make the matter the more playner vnto you, at the Tylt met an armed Lady, with a Courtly Knight, well appoynted at Armes, who menacing his manly might, as though he came to Combat, began to looke about if there were any defendour. The Lady not minding the inuincible courage, and lofty looke of the Champion: gased vpon the renowned Princes, who was there present, debating with her selfe in inward thoughtes, the sodayn aduenture which had happened her, and hauing long looked on this sumptuous spectacle, at length with her selfe, fell into these woordes.

What dooth the Gods delude mee? or hath the infernall ghosts enchaunted me with their fonde illusions? Wake I, or sleepe I? See I, or see I not? What chaunce hath conuicted me? What sodayne sight hath attaynted me? Is this a Goddesse, or a mortall creature? If this be the seemely shee, that the Trumpe of Fame hath so blasted abroade: if this be the second *Saba*, to astonishe the wyse *Salomon?* then hast thou well imployed thy paynes to come and see her. For Report running through the *Orcades*, the golden *American* countrey, and the rytch inhabited Islandes of the East and West *Indias*, ratling in euerie eare this rare rumour, of a gallant and renowned Mayden Queene, that gouerned her Countrey woorthily, her people peaceably, and rightly bare the tytle of inestimable dignitie, sayd in this manner.

The Lady beeing driuen into a great admiration at the presence of this peereles Princesse, vseth her talke in this order.

The Orcades, *the golden* America, *the East and West* Indias.

By west, *a famous Region,*
   with Sea encompast round:
With wealth adornd aboundantly,
   as lyke hath not bene found.
And euerie thing so plentifull,
   in such good order framde:
That this the Isle of happinesse,
   by tytle true is namde.
There, there remaynes the seemlyest Queene,
   that euer nature bred:
In Vertues gyftes excelling farre,
   of all that we haue read.
And more then this, Diana so,
   dooth rule her royall reygne:

That hetherto a Vestall pure,
* she constant dooth remayne.*
Adornd with wisdome woorthily,
* and learning in each case:*
That Fame recordes her Memorie,
* abroade in euerie place.*
Saying, the Queene of Anglia,
* the rarest gemme alyue:*
From all the Creatures on the earth,
* the honour dooth depriue.*
Wherfore arise ye noble rout,
* that long this sight to see:*
You gallant Lordes and Ladyes all,
* in Court where ere you bee.*
And you shall see that seemely Saynt,
* whereof I tell you newes:*
Whose view, the Gods, and mortall men,
* wyll force to stand and muse.*

FINIS.

The Lady dooth suppose that no one deserued rightlye such condigne praise as this peerelesse Princesse.

Was euer so braue a brute blased of the Imperiall *Alexander?* Was his lyfe so meritorious, that it deserued such rare renown? Was puissant *Pompey,* euer so honoured? Or *Iulius Cæsar,* so magnifically adored? Or dyd they all deserue halfe the estimation, that by tytle true this seemely shee maye clayme? No sure, well may their deedes be noted, as a patterne to our eyes: But their lyues shall neuer be regystred, where her Fame is enrolled.

The Lady doubteth whether this is the Princes or no, and at last looketh and espyeth the Champion.

But I, the most vnfortunate creature alyue, heere in a soyle vnknowen to mee, to stand in such great hazard and doubt: Because I know not rightly, whether this be shee or no, yet dooth my minde perswade me, that it were vnpossible to finde her mate. But yet if I knewe that this were shee: I would fetche the rest of my company, that they might be pertakers of my long desired ioyes. But stay, what comely Champion is this so brauely mounted, ready to encounter with his mortall enemie. I wyll attend to see what his comming is, and wherfore he standeth thus to hazard him selfe to Fortune.

◆ The Champion seeing that the Lady

had ended her talke, presumeth neerer, and speaketh to her, as followeth.

IT MAY be fayre Lady, that eyther you hope to purchase prayse, by extolling so much this renowned Queene: Or else you looke for a priuate commodity to counteruayle your bolde attempt, which of them you doo, I knowe not, nor which you are lykelyest to gayne, I can not coniecture: only this I am to aunswer, that (of my self) I thinke no prayse can deseruedly patronize you: without it were more merited, and as for commoditie, you are like to get it where you can, for our charitie is nowe waxen colde.

The Champion speaketh to the Lady, dysdaining her talk passed, and yeeldeth her great rebuke therfore.

In deede I must thus allowe, you Women (for the most part) are giuen to prayse your owne Sex, and though there be no desert: yet wyll you prayse for your pleasure. What heroycall woordes you vsed, are not yet forgotten, and what peremptorie brags you made, yet sticke on my stomacke. You commend this Princes to excell all other, and you seeme to say, that none more rightly dooth deserue it then shee. If you of your

He alleadgeth that women are apte to prayse their Sex.

He vseth threatning woordes, thinking thereby to allay the corage of the Lady.

selfe are able to auouch what is spoken, and of sufficient force to stand to your boasting? doubt not
but you shall be dealt with all before you depart,
and be constrayned to remember your selfe better an other tyme.

He seemeth to extol his Lady abooue the Prin-cesse.

    Haue I condempned my peerelesse *Pollinarda:*
and aduaunced the Fame of this Princes? Haue I
left my natiue Countrey, wherein abound choyse
of delycate Dames, hoping that this should sur-
passe them all? And is it now come to no better
effect? I see Report tatleth as pleaseth her, and
maketh those fooles that thinke them selues most
wyse. Pack vp to *Hungaria,* as wise as thou camest
hyther, and all thy winnings, put in thy purse to
spend when a deere yeere commeth.

❧ *The Lady hearing the Champion*
in such vnlawfull order to contempne the partie in
presence, maketh him an aunswere, thereby to coole
his courage.

The Lady replieth to the Champion, be-cause he seemed so much to commend his Polinarda.

SYR KNIGHT, neither dismayed through your
presumptuous woords, nor yet encouraged
through any vaine hope, yet greatly agreeued at
this your rude behauiour, for my part I am one
who comes to see as well as your selfe, yet dislyke
not so much with my selfe as you doo. Seeme you
to be offended at any thing passed, and extoll you
your *Pollinarda* abooue this gallant Gem? I knowe
it were vnpossible she should make any comparison, and I knowe this so vertuous: that she can not

be her equall. Wherfore if your heart be hardened, that you dare abyde the breakfast that I shall bestowe on you, and your minde so misbeleeuing that it wyll not be reformed: I wyll assay my courage in defence of this Princes, and force you to confesse you haue chosen too hard a choyse.

The Lady biddeth battell to the Champion in defence of her cause.

¶ *The Champion perceyuing the Lady*
so wylling to stand to her woords passed, and that
by force of Armes she would mayntaine
her cause: replyeth.

LADY, if your courage be so correspondent, and your manhood so equiualent, that you dare seeme to auouch your preter presumption, though small honour I shall gayne by conquering a Woman, and no victorie to speake of, it shall be to vanquishe you: yet wyll I teach you how you shall behaue your selfe an other time, and how to beware to make your choyse so hard.

The Champion taketh the offer of the Lady, wylling to enter Combat.

The Lady replyeth.

As for that syr Knight, we shall deale well inough. Now God assist me in this my enterprise, and as I know my quarrell good and lawfull: so hope I the victorie shall be lawdable and gainfull. Thinke not syr Knight, although God hath giuen the greater courage, the more magnanimitie, and the bolder behauiour to your Sex: he hath vtterly reiected the weaker vesselles.

The Lady prayeth for asistance.

In steede of your courage, he hath indued vs with comely condicions, and in place of magnanim-

She applieth her gifts equiualent to his gifts.

itie, he hath graffed womanly modestie: and for your bolde behauiour, he hath bestowed on vs bountifull beautie. So that aspect our beautie: your boldnesse is blunted, respect our modestie: your magnanimitie is but meane, and our comely conditions, wyll soone quayle your courage, and as howe. A Gentleman voyde of Vertue: his behauiour is wurse then a Begger, a meane person adorned with vertue: is a precious Iewell abooue such a Gentleman. Therefore may it rightly be sayde, and sufficiently auouched, that vertulesse Gentillytie: is wurse then Beggerie.

Vertulesse Gentillytie is wurse then Beggerie.

You syr for example, if any iot of Gentillytie, or any signe of humanitie, seemed to be extant in you: you would vse your talke with more discrecion, and demonstrate that which I perceyue is not in you. Is it your bolde behauiour that dooth purchase you prayse? Is it your melancholy magnanimitie, that maketh you euer the more manfull? Or is it your craking courage, that wyll make you euer the sooner commendable? No, in steede of these place honest humanitie: and then I warrant you shall not seeme so haughtie, for bolde behauiour, vse knightly courtesie: and then your deedes wyll appeere more woorthy, for your mysused manhoode, frequent decent magnanimitie: and then your Fame shall be wytnessed accordingly, and for your craking courage, vse Courtly ciuilitie: then shall you be honoured, where now you are nothing esteemed. But as your Countrey is barbarous: so is your behauiour, and as an Ape cloathed in a coate of golde, by his condicions is an Ape styll: So good talke ministred to one that careth not therefore: is euen better well spared then euyll spent.

The Lady chargeth him with greater matters then he looked for.

The Lady heere learneth him a lesson.

¶ *The Champion incensed with great*
anger, commeth neerer the Lady, saying.

AVAVNT presumptuous peasant, seemest thou to vse chyldishe woordes to me? Thinkest thou I wyll be taught of such a Varlet as thou? No, Ile soone coole your courage, therefore delay no longer, but defend thy selfe.

The Champion scorning the Ladies good talke, aunswereth.

The Lady.

Since neyther freendly councell, nor wisdome of thine owne selfe is able to warne thee, but that thou wylt hazard thy hap in hope to conuince me: defend thy selfe manfully, and I as womanly, so that begin when thou please, for I am perfectly prouided.

¶ *The Champion rydeth to the one*
end of the Tylt, and she to the other, and there they deale according as the order and custome is therof, after halfe a score Staues be broken: the Champion was throwen beside his Horse, to whome the Lady came thus saying.

WHAT Syr, is *Miles Gloriosus*, or triumphing *Thraso*, who thought it were vnpossible to pull his pearched plumes, or to cease his corragious countenaunce: nowe brought to so bad a banquet? Was this he who thought him selfe nothing inferiour to *Alexander*, as puissant as *Pompey*,

The Lady hauing vanquished the Champion sayth thus.

as hautie as *Hanniball, Hector* or *Hercules*, as couragious as *Cæsar*, as stoute as *Sampson* or *Scipio:* And nowe foyled at the handes of a Woman? Where is now thy brauerie? Where is thy vaine vaunting? Where is thy presumptuous, peremptorie perswasions? Where are now all thy manly motions? Now dasht amyd the dust? now sent to seeke succour, and thou and all thy might now subiect to my valiancy? How sayst thou, wylt thou reuolt thy former woordes, and content thy selfe to yeelde submission to this peerelesse Princes: or dye the death which thou hast rightly deserued?

The Champion seeing himself in
such a pittifull plight, and that all this whyle he had maintayned a wrong opinion, desired the Lady he might stand vp, and then spake as followeth.

The Champion ashamed of his bolde presumption desireth that they woulde heare his sorrowfull discourse.

RENOWNED Princes, and you most woorthy Lady, as my fact is so faultie, that I can craue no forgiuenesse, and my deede so desperatly doone, that it deserueth due discipline: yet am I to desire you to permyt me a lyttle patience, and to ponder my woordes at your curteous pleasure. First, where folly so guided me, and selfe wyll so blinded me, that I was lead with euerie lewde report, and euerie tatling tale, I not minding the rare vertues resident, in the Princely person whome I haue so haynously offended: let my tongue run at lybertie, where nowe I repent me.

Next, thinking mine owne manhoode sufficient to contend bothe against Men and Monsters: made me to commend my *Polinarda*, whome I nowe perceyue is farre inferiour. Let therefore my cause be construed at your clemencie, let pittie pleade my case, though I be nothing woorthy, and I vowe whyle life lasteth to her such dutifull alleageaunce: that I hope you wyll count my seruice woorthy commendation. In so dooing, that valiant trayne which I brought with me, who are not farre hence attending my comming: shall and wyll be all contented to serue at your pleasure.

He repenteth that he praysed so much his Polinarda.

¶ *The Lady seeing the dutifull showe*
of submission in the Knight, commeth to him, saying.

WELL syr Knight, in hope that your after seruice shall prooue so permanent as heere you haue auouched, and that you euer hereafter in this peerelesse Princes cause, wyll bothe lyue and dye, I dare pronounce that you are pardoned, and that your offence shall be no more remembred.

The Lady commeth to the Champion, pronouncing him pardon, in hope of his amendment.

Cæsar got him such a noble name, through his great compassion, and that made *Cicero* so much to commend him. *Licurgus*, when he had his eye put out, by the neglygence of *Alcander:* commaunded that his first offence should be forgiuen, he would be more heedefull in the next. *Eusebius*, wounded to the death with a stone, throwen from the hand of a Woman: on his death bed

Cicero in Oratione Pro rege Deiotaro. *Alcander who put out* Licurgus *eye.* Eusebius.

forced his freendes to sweare, that they would not harme her for it. I may lykewise alleage the woordes of *Virgill* to thee: *Forsan et hoc olim meminisse iuuabit:* and that the sentence of *Euripides* wyll byd thee beware: *Dulce est meminisse malorum.* Nowe is thy first fault forgiuen, in hope of amendment, so that rather prayse shall be purchased by pardoning thine offence: then that rigour should rule to exact on so penitent an offender. Therefore behold, when Iustice sayth strike: Mercie by mildnesse dooth stay the swoord, and when a crime is commited deseruing death: Pitty dooth woork on the offenders behalfe. Therefore whyle thou lyuest, homage her whose mercifull minde, wyll not reuenge with rygor: for that Vertue hath caused her to pittie thine estate, and thou and all that are her dutifull Subiectes: say, *God saue our most woorthy Queene.* Therefore goe your way, and fetche the rest of your trayne, and so wyll I bring with me all my noble Ladyes, and then will we goe together, to procure some farther pastime.

¶ *After they had bothe brought theyr*

traynes, they fell to a freshe Tournament, and so ended this Deuise.

Zelauto.

NOW syr, haue I not wearied you with this long and tedious discourse? Tell me I pray you how lyke you of it? Is it not woorthy to be caryed in remembraunce, because it is such an excellent deuise?

Astræpho.

Credit me syr, it is the proprest deuise that euer I heard of, and if it shall please you to bestowe the same on me: I wyll giue you as gallant a discourse to cary with you.

Zelauto.

Syr, any thing I haue is at your commaundement, and I would it were so deere a gyft, as I could finde in heart to bestowe on you.

Astræpho.

I thanke you for your good wyll hartily. But doo her noble Peeres and Lords that are about her, often vse to recreate her person with such braue and straunge deuises?

Zelauto.

Syr, those gallant youthes doo, and haue bestowed aboundaunce in the pleasing of her Maiestie, and are so well contented ther withall: that

surely it surpasseth any mans wit to giue them
prayse according to theyr desert.

Astræpho.

But dyd you euer come in acquaintaunce with
any of those noble Gentlemen?

Zelauto.

Zelauto *telleth
how much bound he
was to a noble Lord in
the English Court.*
Yea Syr, and am much bound to one of them in
especiall, who sure in magnanimitie of minde, and
valure of courage, representeth in that famous
Land, a second *Cæsar*, to the view of all that know
him. And a lyttle before I departed out of that
woorthy Countrey, I wrote a few verses in the
commendation, of that vertuous Mayden Queene:
and also I wrote a few other in prayse of that
noble Lord, to whome I am bound for his singuler
bounty.

Astræpho.

I pray you Syr, if those verses be not out of
your remembraunce: let me heare some part of
them?

Zelauto *writ
verses in the prayse of
the Queen.*
Zelauto.

That you shall, wherfore marke what I wryt in
the prayse of the English Queene.

¶ Zelauto *heere telleth to* Astræpho,
the verses that he wrote in the commendation of the Englishe Queene.

If eyes may iudge, and minde may full suppose,
     the Vertues rare, that I of late haue seene:
Then pen at large, may perfectly disclose,
     the seemely honour of a Virgin Queene.
Whose perfect prayse deserues to be vnfolde:
And blasde abroade in trumpe of beaten Golde.

The Graces *three attendant stand at beck,*
     Diana *dooth her royall raygne support:*
Vertue *dooth stand, all vice to countercheck,*
     and Modestie *beares sway in all her Court.*
Trueth *rules aloft, repelling darke debate:*
Iustice *dooth sway the swoord of her estate.*

Prudence *dooth stand, on right side of this* Queene,
     and Temperaunce *a Garland holdes before:*
Then Fortitude *standes ioyntly them betweene,*
     and Tryall *he dooth garde her euermore.*
Peace *on the left syde,* Plentie *on the other:*
Thus seemely they adorne the Queene *their mother.*

Sobrietie *dooth beare the flagge on hye,*
     Virginitie *standes clothde in Vestall white:*
Her trayne behinde borne by Humilitie,
     Pittie *lykewise, waytes on this woorthy wight.*
Thus euerie thing standes in so good a frame:
That farre and neere, dooth spreade her golden Fame.

FINIS.

Astræpho.

Zelauto, beleeue me, I neuer heard in all my lyfe
so many Vertues resident in a mortall creature.
But certaynly as I know your iudgement is excellent in such matters: so I confesse agayne, that had
I not heard it of you, I would not haue beleeued it.
But now Syr, I pray you let me heare the verses
which you wrote in commendation of that noble
Gentleman, whome you praysed so much lykewise.

Zelauto.

That you shall, and I would I were able by pen
to prayse, or by paynes to requite his singuler
great curtesie.

¶ *Heere* Zelauto *rehearseth the verses that*
he wrote in the prayse of a certayne Noble Lorde in the
English Court.

If euer Cæsar *had such gallant Fame,*
    or Hanniball, *whose martiall lyfe we read:*
Then in your Honour, I esteeme the same,
    as perfect proofe in vertue and in deede.
My pen vnable is your prayse to paynt:
With Vertues rare, that dooth your minde ac-
    quaynt.

What I haue found, I neede not to expresse,
    what you haue done, I farre vnwoorthy was:

But Nature yet dooth cause me thinke no lesse,
    but that with looue you dyd respect my case.
And such great looue dyd in your heart
    abound:
That straunge it is the freendship I haue found.

Wherfore for aye I Honour your estate,
    and wishe to you, to lyue Argantus *lyfe:*
And all your deedes may prooue so fortunate,
    that neuer you doo taste one iot of stryfe.
But so to lyue, as one free from annoy:
In health and wealth, vnto your lasting ioy.

FINIS.

Astræpho.

Surely, belyke *Zelauto* you haue found great freendshippe at that noble Gentlemans handes. But referring all other matters aside, tell me what became of your Companion, that went with you into England?

Zelauto.

Truly he was so farre in loue with the Countrey, that I could not get him from thence when I departed. And in deede so would I lykewise haue stayde, if my Fathers commaundement had not bene such, which caused me to hasten away, because I would see other Countryes.

Astræpho.

Then you dyd depart shortly after, and left your Companion there?

Zelauto.

Zelauto *taketh shypping into* Persia.

Yea Syr. And from thence I tooke shypping to goe into *Persia*. But many were the myseries that I poore soule abode among the tyrannous *Turkes*.

Astræpho.

Astræpho *seemeth to tell* Zelauto *of his bolde hazarding himselfe in such order.*

But durst you seeme to wander so farre as to put your selfe, in hazard of lyfe among those cruell and bloody *Turkes*. You remembred not belyke your Fathers commaundement, who wylled you to guide your selfe so well: that your returne might be to his eternall ioy, but rather as desperate, hauing a youthfull head and a running wyt, would venture on your owne destruction.

Zelauto.

Zelauto *excuseth his boldnesse as well as he can.*

In deede Syr, who mindeth not the after miserie: wadeth often so farre that he is cleane ouer shooes, so I more vppon pleasure then any other cause: put my selfe to God and good Fortune on that behalfe, yet was I not vnmindfull of my Fathers preceptes, for that I purposed nothing, but found it to my profit.

Astræpho.

They goe to supper.

Well *Zelauto*, it draweth now towarde night, and we haue well spent this tyme in talke. Let vs now goe in, and prouide something for our Supper. And to morrow we wyll discourse of your other aduentures at large.

Zelauto.

I am well contented Syr, and a thousand thankes I yeelde you for your courtesie.

The Author.

Thus hath *Zelauto* and *Astræpho* passed one day in talke together, and now are gone to prouide such necessaries as are needefull to suffice theyr hungrie stomackes: howe they spent the next day: the matter ensuing shall make manifest. Thus yeelding my selfe (gentle Reader) vnto thy courteous construction, and not to a rashe Reporters reprehension: I wishe my woorkes might procure thee as much pleasure, as my good wyll is to woorke thy welfare.
Vale.

Honos alit Artes.

FINIS.   *A. Munday.*

Zelauto.

His Ariuall in *Persia*, his valiant
aduenturing in the defence of a Lady,
condempned for her Christianitie, his
prosperous Perigrination among
the tyrannous Turkes, with
the rest of his Knightly
deedes.

❧ The second part of the
Fountayne of Fame.

Written by A. M.

Honos alit Artes.

The Author, to the curteous

Reader.

WHO but behelde the one syde of *Ianus:* woulde hardlie iudge that he were so rare misshaped. And who but viewed the vpper part of a *Siren:* would think she were a whole woman incorporat. So who but readeth the beginning of a booke: can giue no iudgement of the sequell ensuing. The Fryer in the midle of his sermon, cryed the best was behind: and I hauing tolde you a peece of a tale, say the finest followeth. So, if that you beholde *Ianus* perfectly: you shall see his deformednesse, and if you see all partes of the *Siren:* you shall finde the alteration, lykewise if you reade all the booke: you shall not be deluded by (the best is behinde) but so to reprehend mine excuse. The Printer (you will say) hath painted it full of Pictures, to make it be bought the better: and I say the matter is more meritorious, and therefore you should buy it the sooner. So, if you wyll be ruled by the Printer and me: you shall at no tyme want any of the Bookes.

The homelyest house, may be hansome within: the simplest Garden, may haue Flowers woorth the smelling, and a weather beaten Bulwarke, may hold out the bolde blowes of a well wintered Soldier. Many a good Captayne, may goe in a playne coate, and many an honest man, may walke simply arayed. Therefore, the homlynesse of the house, dooth not reprehend the hansomnesse, the symplenesse of the Garden, condempne the sweet sent of

the Flowers, nor the Bulwark disbase the stoutnes
of the Soldier, lykewise, the playne coate of the
Captaine dooth not diminish his manhood: nor the
meane aray of the Citizen, impayre any of his honesty: Neyther dooth the bluntnes of my Booke, altogether condempne me: nor the meane methode
of the matter, diminish any iot of the good wyll of
the Author, you can haue no more of a Catte but
her skyn: nor of me more then I am able to doo.
Well, I wyll not trouble you with wresting
many woords, nor hinder you from hearing
that which ensueth: you haue free entraunce into the Orchard, pluck where
you please, looue where you lyke, and
fancy where you finde fyttest.

FINIS.

Your freend.
A. Munday.

The second part of the delycate
Disputation between two noble Gentlemen of Italy.

Astræpho.

NOW Syr *Zelauto*, you haue seene, the whole courtesy, that I your poore freende can show you, to feast you with Fortunes fare (I call it so) because as to day I haue it, and to morrow it is vncertayn, therefore it commeth by sodayne chaunce, and also to lodge you in my carefull coutch, harde and vnpleasant, the furniture therto belonging all of mosse and leaues, yet well dooth it content me, because I haue vsed my selfe therto, to you I knowe it is straunge, and no meruayle, because the Princely pleasures that is in your famous fathers Mansion, as yet stick vpon your stomack. My selfe, hauing remayned heere full foureteene yeeres and more, haue cleane forgot, my preter delightes, my wanton conceyts, and my layes of Looue. Now to the sprouting sprayes I commend my sute, the Hylles, the Dales, the Rockes, the Clyffes, the Cragges, yea, and the gallant Ecchoes resound of this solitary Wyldnesse, they and none but they can witnesse of my woe. In Court I serued, to my small auayles, I sued to a selfe wylled Saint, I complayned, and it was not regarded. But heere I lyue as Prince within my selfe, not foe to any, nor none to me. I adore my God. I feast my selfe as well as I can, as for my garmentes, though they be homely, yet are they

Astræpho in the morning beginneth to talk with Zelauto, *desiring him to accept in good part his homely entertainment.*

He showeth how he needeth not to accept of coyne, for because he hath Nobody to barter withal.

healthfull, for Silken sutes, are not to wander among the bryery brakes withall. What care I for money, I haue Nobody to barter withall, my Hoste asketh me no money when I ryse from breakfast, dinner or supper, then what should I doo with it? If in your carefull Citties, you as lyttle regarded, your coyne as I: you should not haue so much extorcion, so much brybing to Officers, so much wrangling and iarring among the common sort, so much encroching one vpon another, and to conclude, you should not haue so many diuellish deuises frequented, therfore I doo not aspect for my priuate commoditie, I lyue not heere by pride or by vsurie, but I take all contentedly, so to no man am I enemie. This homely discourse, for a mornings good morrowe I trust will suffice, now must I desire you to proceede in your promised affayres, touching the rest of your mishappes.

Money in Cities causeth much mischeefe, discencion among the commons, discorde among freendes, and such lyke iniuries.

Zelauto.

Courteous Sir, if my slender habilitie, were of such and so great a puissaunce, as might but seeme to counteruayle the large and inestimable courtesie, that I haue founde at your hands vndeseruedly: I might then the bolder behaue my selfe in your company. But as where nothing is to be had, the King looseth his right: euen so I hauing nothing, yeeld my selfe to your courteous consideration, always remembred, that if it shall please God to sende such successe, as of long I haue looked for: I doubt not (though not able to satisfie the whole, wherin I am indebted) yet to recompence the greatest part as neere as I can. And this by the way to assure your selfe, though lothe to spend so much

Zelauto yeeldeth innumerable thanks for the great courtesies that he hath found, beeing but in deede a straunger.

lyp labour in promysing you preferment, doubt not but in heart I will remember you, and that to your contentment.

Astræpho.

Syr *Zelauto*, heere needeth no such thanks, if I could bestow so much of you, as my poore heart would wyllingly affoord: I doubt not but then you would thanke me. In the meane whyle, take as you finde, welcome your selfe though you be not bidden, shut vp the sacke when it is but halfe full, and giue God thankes for all. But proceede I pray you as touching your promise, for I greatly desire to heare what after happened you.

Astræpho *desirous to heare the rest of his trauayles: remembreth him of his former promise.*

Zelauto.

I shall satisfie your aspectation wyllingly, but giue eare I pray you, and marke it attentiuely, for you shall heare the tenour of a straunge and tragicall Commedy.

Heer Zelauto *telleth how he departed from the royall Realme of* England, *and arriued at* Zebaia *in* Persia, *and of the great courtesy that he found with his Host* Manniko Rigustello, *and also of his wife named* Dania.

BEING departed from my Companion, and from that thrise renowned Realme of England, after many hard and diffycill passages: I arriued at *Zebaia*, a gallant and braue Cittie in *Persia*. Beeing come thyther, alas I wyst not what to say,

Zelauto *his comming to* Zebaia *in* Persia, *to the house of one* Manniko Rigustello, *who lodged Christians.*

the people so gased vpon me, as though they would haue eaten me, so at last I entred into the signe of the *Gorgons* head, which is a house of lodging for Straungers. When I came in, I found my Hoste and his Wife sitting by the fire at supper, I saluted them in their owne language as well as I could, mary mine Hostesse was a *Florentine*, and she did quickly perceyue what countreyman I was, wherefore she rose vp, and very courteously bad me welcome, so presently I was had vp into a Chamber, and a good fire made, then I sate down and communed with mine Hostes.

The hostes of the house a Christian and a Florentin.

The talke betweene mystres *Dania* and *Zelauto* in his Chamber.

The hostes and Zelauto conferreth together about his comming to that place, and informeth him of the lawes and orders of that City.

Syr (quoth she) as the sight of a Christian in this place, is a thing of great lyking vnto me: euen so are you welcome, although as yet vnacquainted. But neyther to stand vpon the nicenesse of Rethoricall gloses, nor to trifle the time with long and doubtfull delayes, this I am to enforme you, we are heere subiect vnder a Law, to which Law, wyll we, nyll we, we must obey, the Law dooth thus farre stretch in charge, that no Christian must abide in the Cittie abooue ten dayes, if longer, to their owne peryll, in which tyme, the Hoste must be sworn for his good vsage, and to see if that he keepe due and decent behauiour in his house. Now Syr, you hauing taken vp your lodging heere: my Husband is vpon his good lyking to giue his woord for you. Thinke not Gentleman that I speake to discourage you, for you shall finde your selfe heere as well vsed as in your owne Countrey,

The hostes proffereth herself to be his freend.

I am my selfe a Christian borne, and wyll stand
your freend in more then I wyll nowe make my
vaunt of: therefore (by the way) I giue you first
to vnderstand our Lawes, of other matters we shall
the better discourse afterwardes. Gentlewoman
(quoth I) I would that my simple and meane behauiour, might once be woorthy to deserue, the
courtesie of such a freendly entertaynment, and
surely in the informing me of the Lawes and Cus-
tomes of your Citie: you haue doone me no small
pleasure, for otherwise, I might haue by some one
occasion vnwittingly violated them. But now since
you (on meere courtesie) hath doone thus much
for me: I am to yeelde you a thousand thankes.
Well syr (quoth she) then if I might be so bolde, I
would enter into a lyttle talke with you. Truly
Gentlewoman (quoth I) you are not so wylling: as hartily welcome, therefore say what pleaseth you.

Zelauto giueth her great thankes for her courtesie.

Then syr (quoth she) since your patience hath
pardoned my rash attempt: I am the bolder without blushing to craue such courtesie at your
handes, as to rehearse of whence you are, from
whence you come, what mooued you to visite this
place, and whether you minde to trauayle. Sus-
pect no subtyll Sophistrie in this my demaund
(good syr) but rather impute my boldnesse to
countrey behauiour, and to one that wisheth your
welfare.

She demandeth of what countrey he is, and wherfore his comming is, and whether hee minded to make his iourney.

Gentlewoman (quoth I) to dissemble were no
part of freendly familiaritie, to lye, would impayre my name and credite, to tell trueth also, may
heere perhappes to returne to myne owne endamagement, but buylding my assuraunce on your
Christian fidelitie, and hoping you will not seeke

Zelauto reposing a good beleefe in his hostesse, because shee was a christian, openeth to her of whence he was, and how he had traueyled other countreyes, and howe hee meant to traueile, tyl his tyme were expyred.

to woorke my harme wilfully, but wyll rather adiuuate me in my necessitie: to you wyll I vnfolde the sum of my secretes. First I am a *Venetian* borne, and my Father, if lyuing (as I hope he be) thereof is Duke, my youthfull minde beeing addicted to see forrayne Countreyes: left my Father, and tooke my selfe to trauayle. So after the view of other Countreyes: Fortune hath sent me hether, where I must be no long abyder, because fowre yeeres and more are fully expyred, and my tyme dooth amount but vnto sixe yeeres, and to aunswer whether I shall goe from hence: I can not, because I must craue your good and freendly direction in my voyage, that I may escape from mine enimies: and safely returne home into my Countrey.

She aunswereth him verie honestly and ciuilly, so it drewe at length to suppertime.

In deede syr (quoth she) I can not blame you, to keepe your selfe so secrete, if you be discended of so noble a house, and for my part, you shall be iniured by no way, but rather aduaunced, and if lyfe, goodes, or what euer else may pleasure you: be bolde, for they are ready at your commaundement. By this tyme it waxed somewhat darke, and supper was ready, so the meate beeing serued vp into my Chamber, the Hoste came, and he, his wife and I, supped altogether.

❧ *The talke which* Manniko Rigustello *the host,* Dania *his wife, and* Zelauto *had together at Supper.*

The Hoste beeing at supper with Zelauto, knowing he was a Christian, and had a

MANNIKO RIGVSTELLO the Hoste, sitting at the Table, and seeing that I was a Christian, he beeing one him selfe that of long tyme endeuoured to become a Christian: desired me, (if I coulde) to rehearse some part of the Scripture, whereby he might receyue comfort and consolation, for the want of which he was long time troubled and vexed in his spyrit. Quoth I, though not so able as I would I were, yet wyll I reueale such things vnto you, as I haue no doubt but you shall be comforted thereby, and I wyll helpe to mitigate your wounded conscience, by the sweet and blessed promises of our Lord and sauiour Iesus Christe, a soueraigne medicine against all frailties of the vyle and voluptuous fleshe.

good minde to the same him selfe, entreth into talke with him.

❧ *Heere* Zelauto *rehearseth to* Astræpho *the comfortable talke that he vsed to his Hoste* Manniko Rigustello, *and of the conuersion of his Hoste.*

AFTER that God of his infinit goodnesse and mercy, had framed all things according to his heauenly will and pleasure, as first the day and night, next the trees, the earth, the sea, the fishes, the fowles, and all liuing beasts: then made he Man the Image of his owne lykenes, and graffed into him reason and vnderstanding, whereby he excelled all the creatures of the earth, insomuch, that he gaue him the domination ouer all other creatures, as the Oxe bothe to labour for him, and to be sustentation to his body likewise, the Horse to beare his wearie carkase, after his tedious labour, and other creatures beside for his behoofe and nourishment.

The creation of man. Gene. 1.

Man made a gouernor. The beastes to labour for him, and to be his foode lykewise.

Man, what a losse hee had.

Man, cast out of Paradise.

God yet would not leaue vs succorlesse, but sent his Prophetes to preache to vs, then his Christ to pay the raunsome of our sinnes and what greeuous tormentes he did abyde for vs: yet we do not seeke to amende our naughtie lyuing, but dayly sinne more and more.

Zelauto telleth him what cruelty they vse to a poore member of Christes body, when they take him.

But man amyd all his gallant ioyes, receyued so sharpe and so heauy a fall: that for euer he lost his paradisall pleasures. Before, lyuing at lybertie, wanting nothing to his prosperity, was now driuen into such a perplexitie, that he must eate his bread in the sweat of his browes, tyll the ground by his wearie labour, beside, sustayning the wrathfull countenaunce of his heauenly Creator, that before was bent towarde him so loouingly: nowe cast out vtterly, ashamed to come before his Maiestie, so horrible was his sinne and iniquitie, that the quantitie of his losse to vs is vnspeakable.

But what of that, dyd God for euer after leaue vs desolate? dyd he send vs no comfort to succour vs? Yes, yes, his Prophets to preache to vs, lastly, his deere Sonne to ransome vs, who when we were at the brinke of vtter destruction, payed the price of his precious blood, to redeeme vs. What mockings? what scoffinges? what raylinges? what spytting in the face? what whipping? what crowning with thorne? what nailing on the Crosse? and what tyrannous tormentes dyd hee meekely, patiently, loouingly, gently, yea, and wyllingly suffer for our sinnes. But alas how lyttle doo we regard it? we that knowe there is a God, and a punishment due to our sinnes: seeke not to amend our lyues. You that lyue in darknesse, and not able to attayne to so cleere lyght: how wilfully, how wantonly, how wickedly you leade your lyues because you wyll not knowe this. When you catche a Christian, a member of that sweete body that suffred all these torments: then triumphe you, what mercilesse tormentes he must abyde, alas, my heart bleedeth for to thinke on, howe tyrannically you can finde in heart to vse him?

And whereof groweth this great crueltie you vse? only for want of the knowledge of God. If you knew what God is: you would then consider with your selues, howe you should doo to an other man as you would be done to your selfe.

If you knewe God, you would neuer call on such a vaine thing as *Mahomet* is: but on the true God, he which lyueth and reygneth euerlastingly. If you knew God: you would then beleeue in his Christe, (whose name you can not abyde) and then you would consider what and how many greeuous tormentes he suffered for you, and then would you rather seeke to increase the members of his body: then to make such hauocke and spoyle of them as you doo. So that if you knew God: you should be partakers with his deere chyldren, in the kingdome of heauen.

Through want of knowledge of God commeth this great tiranny. To knowe God, is to do as we would be done vnto.

To knowe God, to worship him only.

To know God, to beleeue in his Christe.

To knowe God, bringeth lyfe euerlasting.

Manniko Rigustello the Hoste reasoneth with *Zelauto*.

Syr (quoth the Hoste) by this your talke, I am greatly mooued in minde. First, to consider the blindnesse in which I haue lyued. Next to thinke on the happy and blisfull lyfe that you Christians haue. But syr, I haue communed with a great many that haue come hether, and they in deede haue tolde me part of that which euen now you sayde, and haue hartned me verie much, but none that euer came so neere the quicke as you doo: well letting that passe, I am to desire you to infourm me howe I might attayne to so sweete a

The Hoste mooued in minde at the talke of Zelauto: entreth into farder communication with him.

The Hoste desireth to know how he might lykewise become a Christian.

comfort as you haue. If my applyable paynes may
ayde me to purchase it: I vowe no occasion whatsoeuer shall hinder me.

Zelauto.

Zelauto *glad to
heare the Hosts good
zeale, yet desireth him
to cease of that talke
tyll some other more
conuenient tyme.*

I am right glad (quoth I) to heare that you haue
so good a zeale and intent to the Christian faith,
and my dilligence shall not want to councell you
therein, but as of two extremities, the least is to be
chosen, and of two euilles the wurst to be shunned:
So holde I it best, that at this tyme we leaue to
conferre of these matters, least that when we least
of all thinke, the enimie come to subuert vs. At
this tyme, if you please, let vs vse such delightfull
talke (vsed with moderation) as may well recreate
vs: and no faulte be found therewith, yet think not
(I desire you) but that I will satisfie your requests,
in whatsoeuer you please, and you shall finde me
to doo more for you, then now I minde to make
protestation of. So if you are well instructed, and
I deuoyde of my peryll: you shall winne your
whole wishing, and I purchase no disprofite. How
say you syr, are you contented to graunt to that I
haue spoken?

Manniko Rigustello, the Hoste.

*The Hoste is wel con-
tented with the reply
of* Zelauto, *and
falleth with him into
other talke.*

In deede syr, you say trueth, lyttle sayde is
soone amended, and where the hedge is lowest, the
beastes goe ouer soonest: therfore we wyll ceasse
this talke at this time, and reason therof betweene
our selues secretly. Therfore tell me I pray you,
what was the cause of your comming into this
Countrey, beeing such a soyle, wherin they rather
desire your death, then wish your well fare? and
whether meane you from hence to trauayle?

Zelauto.

Sir (quoth I) you knowe that a youthfull minde is styll ventrous, and desirous to see new sightes, and fashions euery day, wherefore I beeing one more addictted to pleasure then profite, and more desirous of nouelles, then to continew styll in one song: hazarded my selfe to all chaunces, whatsoeuer, and hitherto I haue out stoode them (I thanke God) well inough. What shall followe I know not, what is passed hath bene sufficientlie discharged, but whether I trauayle from hence, is vtterly vnknowen, thus you knowe at large the cause of my trauayles.

Zelauto telleth to the Hoste the cause why hee went thus in trauaile.

We had now sitten at supper not fully halfe an hower, but there came in one, a verie goodly Gentleman, who was Nephew to the *Soldane* of the Cittie, named *Mica Sheffola*, this Gentleman sate downe at the Table, and gaue a verie greeuous sigh, at length looking on me, the blood rose aboundantly in his face, and the teares began to trickle downe his cheekes. My Hostesse *Dania* seeing the pensiue plight of this Gentleman: ran to him, and tooke him about the necke saying. Alas good syr, what meaneth these mestiue motions? What harme is happened that makes you so heauy? Or what cause procureth you to lament in this sort? O tell me good sweete syr, and if any helpe lyeth in me: credit me, I wyll doo it to the verie vttermost of my power. Ah good *Dania* (quoth he) I knowe right well, if thou couldest remedy the matter thou wouldest doo it wyllingly, but the case so standeth, that it is farre from thy power to pleasure me, or any that I knowe, that is able to doo so much for me. Then looked he on me againe,

Mica Sheffola the Nephew of the Soldane came in verie sad and heauy.

The Hostes of the house taketh the Gentleman about the necke to comfort him.

and faine he would haue spoken, but yet he was halfe afrayde, which I seeing, and hearing him say, that a man might pleasure him in the cause of his so great sorrow, I sayd.

Gentleman, Arte and inuencion of man hath framed for euery sore a salue, for euery malladie a medicine, and for euerie disease a cause or remedy for the same. Likewise God, as he hath framed the mouth: so hath he sent meate to sustayne the same with all, and as he sendeth sicknesse to man, so dooth he send him health againe.

Man of him selfe is placed among a multitude of myseries, somtime ready to fall into this euill, then into that, yet is he not left desolate. As God sendeth him myserie: so sendeth he ioye againe, a whyle he scourgeth, and then he ceaseth, a whyle he lowreth, and then he laugheth.

The Phisition first ministreth a sharpe Salue to searche the deapth of the disease, and then he the better and sooner healeth his cure. The Prince a whyle frowneth vppon his Subiect, to declare his authoritie, and to make him to obey: but afterward he vseth his dealinges mercifully. The maister quickeneth vp the dull minde of the Scholler with sharpe woordes, and stripes of the rodde at the first: but afterward he looueth him, and maketh much of him.

Euen so Sir it may be, that some sodeyne chaunce permitted by God hath happened, as to depriue you of some of your deerest freendes, or else that some vnlooked for mischaunce hath happened, which procureth your pensiuenesse, souseth you in sorrowes, and maketh you mone in such mestiue manner. If so it be, thinke not but he which hath sent this Crosse: is able to take it away againe, and that he which causeth you now to lament: wyll at length cause you to laugh.

Therefore neuer wrap your selfe in woes, nor waste your dayes in wayling: For that can but cause the vnquietnesse of the minde, distempera-ture of the body, and lykewise bereaue you of your sences. Pardon my presumption (Syr) I pray you, in that I seeme to meddle in this matter, which to me nothing pertaineth, and that I per-turbe your patience with my friuolous talke. I doubt not but it is as well taken: as it is meant by me and spoken, and as courteously construed, as my poore self pretended. I would be verie loth to haue any heauy, although I can procure them small pleasure, and I would be sorie to see one in sadnesse: if by my meanes I might mooue him to myrth.

He sheweth him howe his great lamenting dooth but bring all his sences out of quiet.

Therefore Syr (although you be to me a straunger, and I haue no commission to examin you in this case, yet as a freend that wisheth you well, and would willingly, woorke your well fare,) if you please to vnfolde the cause that molesteth your minde, and what you thinke is best remedy therfore: I promise you on my fideli-tie, though it were to encounter with any enimie, to procure you a remedy: I would hazard it wyll-ingly. In signe and token wherof, that my deede shall make manifest my woorde: I offer you the hand of a true and faithfull Christian.

He courteouslie offreth him self, to pleasure him by any means that lyeth in him to doo.

℞ Mica Sheffola *the* Soldanes *Nephew* *replyeth to the courteous offer of* Zelauto.

WHEN the Gentleman had well pondered my tale, and beeing one (as I was informed by my Hostesse before) that I neede not to doubt of, because he was a good Christian him selfe, but he durst not be knowen therof: tooke my hand and courteously kyssed it, and then began to say.

The Gentleman kisseth Zelautoes *hand, and then beginneth freendly to talke with him.*

Syr, I am glad of your Christian company, but sorie for your beeing in so succorles a soyle, and although you be a straunger: yet to me the welcommest man alyue. I haue noted well your freendly talke, and wishe I were able any way to requite it, neuertheles you shall finde me more your freend then I entend to boast of, and I will awarde any extremitie, that may heere seeme to hurt you, in hope when you haue heard it: you wyll doo your good will to helpe it.

The Gentleman openeth the cause of his sadnesse to Zelauto.

It is so syr (as your Hoste can credibly wytnesse) that I am Nephew to the *Soldane Neoreo*, who gouerneth this Cittie, and one, who with him am able to doo you a pleasure, but at this tyme, Fortune hath frowned so frowardly: that she hath dasht the cheefe of my desires in the dust. I haue a very gallant, godly and vertuous Gentlewoman to my Sister, who because of her Christian beleefe, and constant auouching of the same: is condempned by the Lawe, and to morrowe shee must loose her life. Yet hath the *Soldane* thus much graunted, that if any one whatsoeuer, dare venture him selfe against a Champion by force of Armes to set her free: shee shall vpon his good successe be restored at lybertie. To take this case in hand I

His syster for her christian beleefe appointed to death.

knowe no one dare be so bolde, there are many which wyllingly would: but that they doubt to be suspected thereby, my selfe dare wyllingly venture the cause: but that if I should conquere the enimie, myne Vnckle the *Soldane* would conspire my death by some meanes, so that seeing no way to adiuuate this extremitie, I am fully perswaded shee shall dye the death. And to request you heerein, I willingly would not, for that I know it were the losse of your life: which (on my Christian fidelytie) I would be lothe to heare of, much lesse to be the procurer thereof. Wherfore (good syr) tell me the best councell you can, what may be done in this doubtfull matter?

Zelauto.

I hauing heard the Gentlemans sorrowfull tale, and considered the distressed case of that famous and woorthy Lady: thought, that if I lost my lyfe in defence of my faith, my Captayne Christe would purchase me the greater reward. Again, if the Lady were so constant, to abyde such mercilesse tormentes as her owne kyndred, and the residue of her enimies would wyllingly lay vpon her, and all for the zealous Christianitie which remayned in her vertuous brest: I should deseruedly reape a great reproche, if I could and would not seeke to mittigate her miseries. Therfore wholy committing the cause to Gods omnipotencie, and not accoumpting of my life, to set foorth his glorie: I enterprised the matter courragiously, in assured hope to foyle the enimie. And if that afterwarde my death by any meanes should be conspired: I would referre all to the wyll of the almightie, for that death were vnto me aduauntage,

Summa virtutis
Potestas est.

and life nothing meritorious. The learned say: *Cui comes virtus non est, is animo facile cadit a fortuna percussus*. The minde therefore adorned with vertue: wyll neuer be timerous of that which shall rayse his eternall honour, for after death is the glory of a mans preter dayes wytnessed, as it is

Mors non est formi-
danda.

rightly sayde: *Viuit post funera Virtus,* and euen so I encouraged, through the good hope I had sustayned: I made no accoumpt of this miserable mortality, but addressed my selfe to set the Lady at lybertie, and so turning to the Gentleman, I sayd.

Zelauto *replyeth to
the demaund of the
Gentleman.*

Syr, as I am wylling to worke your well fare, So am I doubtfull of my destruction, and as I may pleasure you to your perpetuall profite: so may I hinder my selfe to my helplesse harmes: You say your selfe, the aduenture is so aduerse: that on bothe sides it bringeth death, though the Lady enioye her lybertie: the Conquerer must abyde captiue, therefore neither can the Lady like her delyuerie: nor her Champion his harde choyse.

Againe, if I (beeing a Christian) should conceiue so good a courage, as to venture on my valiancy, to redresse her emminent myserie: I doubt least a farder inconuenience might be to her alotted, and to me a death, that (albeit dying) should styll lyue, this is to be doubted, and if it might be possible, woorthy to be preuented. But nowe Syr to assure your selfe, what a Christian courage can comprehend, and to satisfie the sorrowes, that you and your freendes haue sustayned, thus much (more for your freendly fauor, then any gaine I hope for, yea and more for the good lyking that I haue conceyued, then for any ryches wherewith you are able to reward me) I dare

hazard my selfe to defend your Syster, and stand
to the peryll that my presumption may procure
me. Wherefore if it shall please you, to prouide me
of such needefull necessaries, as such a matter may
amount vnto, and you and she together to pray
for the prosperitie, which God in this fight is able
to lend me: I will aduenture, not doubting of good
successe.

When the Gentleman had heard the freendly
offer which I made him, and vppon so small acquaintaunce, I would doo so much for him: he
imbraced me, and sayde vnto me in this order.

Woorthy Sir, neyther know I how to gratifie
so gentle a gift: nor how to remember you with a
iust reward, for that abyllitie wanteth to performe
the one: but good will is ready to discharge the
other. Howe am I bound in dutie to your singuler
humanitie, that more regarded the solytarie state
of my Sister: then the prosperitie of your
woorthy selfe? If the woordes of a *Turke*, may so
perfectly pierce your heart with pittie: how much
more is a Christian able to obtayne of you? and if
the dyrefull distresse of a Heathen Lady, can
cause your Christian courage so to aduenture:
how are your famous Matrones bound to vaunt of
so valiaunt a Champion? Yet muse I, how beeing a
Christian, you durst make your selfe manifest to
me, not deeming any doubtfull dealing, nor thinking any forgerie to remayne in me, but that your
God gaue you grace, to know your freendes from
your foes, and a dissembler from a direct dealer.
It may be I boast of my selfe more then beseemeth
me, and crake with a countenance, not of any constancie, and it may be, you thinke me so vaine
glorious a vaunter, or some fantasticall fellow,

Mica Sheffola rendreth vnto Zelauto great thankes for his so large and courteous proffer.

He museth howe hee durst make him selfe knowen.

that dwelling among naughtie neyghbours, who conceale my commendation: I play the Parasite with mine owne mouth to extoll my selfe.

I knowe not, thought is free to euerie one, and euerie man may conceyue according to his minde, I haue not the rayne to rule your reason, nor the lybertie to let your tongue from speaking, fewe woordes among freendes (they say) is fittest, and lyttle sayd is soone amended, I can not discouer what I deeme you deserue: Nor I minde not to mencion what mendes I wyll make you. If you prooue so fortunate, as to succour my Sister, and your God haue so agreed that you shall be victor: It shall be verie hard but I will reskew you from their rigor, and my selfe take part of your paynes whatsoeuer. And heere in token, my woords shall turne into deedes, I giue you the hande of a *Turke*, chaunged to a Christian. With you to lyue and lacke, with you to be true and trusty, *Vsque ad mortem.*

Syr (quoth I) neyther doo my deedes deserue halfe the good report you haue vttered, nor my simple self woorthy to weare such commendation. But as the Bryer beeing touched, followeth so farre as it can: so I beeing praised, presume as farre as honesty may holde me. What I haue promised, I purpose to performe, and what you haue offered, I shall still accoumpt of: in the morning let be brought such defence as shall serue the turne: and I am heere your Champion ready to the Combat.

Our Hoste hauing sitten all this whyle, and heard what woords had passed betweene vs: right ioyfull that I would aduenture for the Lady, sayd thus. Now surely Gentleman, were the vttermost

He yeeldeth the iudgement of his woords passed to the courteous construing of Zelauto.

He giueth to Zelauto his hand to be a Christian, and with him to taste of any troubles.

Zelauto desireth him in the morning to bring his armor, and he wyll discharge his promise.

The Hoste rendreth thankes to Zelauto.

of my abilytie, able to aunswer your singuler courtesie, or any action (whatsoeuer) I your poore freend could performe: you should not finde me so forward to vtter the same, as I would be in the verifying thereof, but in token that I would discharge what heere I haue spoken: I, and all mine resteth at your commaundement. Then turned he to the Gentleman saying. And you Syr (for your part) haue good occasion to thinke your comming fortunate, and your time not yll bestowed: when you finde a freend so ready to graunt your request. I should thinke you verie much discourteous, and that small humanity harbored in you, if you should seeme to be obliuious of so courteous an offer, but I knowe your wisdome wyll way the matter so wisely: that my simple selfe neede not to make mencion thereof, yet as one that wisheth your good credite should be blased by your good deedes: and that so noble a Gentleman should not be lightly remembred: I was so bolde to interrupt your patience with my friuolous talke, and to occupie the tyme, better then to stande ydle.

The Hoste speaketh to Mica Sheffola.

With that, my Hostesse *Dania*, courteouslie kyssing my hand, beganne to say as followeth. Woorthy Syr, neyther would I wishe you to surmyse my woordes spoken of flatterie: nor that you should suppose I speake otherwise then my minde serueth me, neyther you noble *Sheffola* to misconster my meaning: but to accept as my talke shall giue occasion. First, the outward apparaunce of this gallant Gentlemans humanitie: maketh ample discouerie of true nobillitie. Next, the hauty courage that consisteth in his valiaunt brest: argueth that his Parentes are of hye degree, for we

The Hostesse speaketh to Zelauto, *and to* Mica Sheffola.

The Hostesse her great good wyll to Zelauto.

all beeing straungers, and you most of all: his seemely selfe to take vppon him to discharge so great a taske, as the losse of his owne lyfe to succour your Syster: mee thinkes you are vnable to counteruayle his courtesie, who forceth not his lyfe to defend Christianitie. Therefore Syr, for euer commaund me and mine, farder then now I meane to make mencion of.

Zelauto thanketh his Hoste and Hostes for theyr good opinion.

My freendes (quoth I) your good wyll I see is great, and your affection so feruent: that you imbolden me to perfourme that which I haue made vaunt of, wherefore you Syr, may depart when you please, and fayle not to send such thinges as are needefull, and that verie timely in the morning.

Mica Sheffola *departeth from* Zelauto *and goeth to the prison to his syster.*

Syr (quoth he) your minde shall be fulfylled, to the vttermost that you haue required, and nowe wyll I goe to the prison to my solytarie Syster, to comfort those cares that this harde happe procureth, so shall I dryue her from doubt, and procure her to prayer, that her Champion may prooue so valiaunt, as to vanquishe her enimies. In the meane tyme I committe you Syr, to your God, who I pray to strengthen you in your attempt, and so mine Hoste and Hostesse bothe fare well.

Zelauto confirmeth *the Hoste in the Christian fayth.*

The Gentleman beeing thus departed, and the howre of rest approching: I entred with mine Hoste into a Chamber, secretly betweene our selues, and there exhorted him in the best manner I could, so that my dillygent labour bestowed: brought him to a good beleefe, and that he was fully pretended to lyue and dye in the good counsayle I gaue him.

Well, all that night, I went not to bedde, but on my knees with heaued handes, made my peticions to my God almightie, to sheelde me safe from the tyrannie of my mortall enimies.

In the morning, the Gentleman returned agayne, and brought with him a verie gallant Courser, a coate of Complet Armour, a Sheelde, and other necessaries. When he was entred my Chamber, verie courteouslie, he sayd. Albeit (woorthy Syr) I can not comprehend my long expectation in all poyntes, but that I fayle in the fulfilling some part thereof: I doubt not but you wyll respect the breuitie of the tyme, and allowe a reasonable excuse, contayning nothing but trueth. And though this furniture is not so fyt as I would it were, nor my entraunce so honestly discharged, as it might haue beene: I hope you wyll deeme the one as farre as might could maintayne it, and accoumpt the other but for want of good manners: neuerthelesse, if you beare with my boldnesse on this behalfe, perchaunce it may be hereafter a sufficient warning.

Mica Sheffola returneth in the morning, with the Armour for Zelauto.

Fyrst Sir, yester night after I departed, I went to the prison to see my Sister, whom I found nothing fainting, though feare were so nye: nor in ought to dismay at the terror of death, but rather reioycing, that her race was so neere run, and to leaue mortality for eternal felicity, saying vnto me. O brother, neither molest your minde with any mazednes, nor subdue your selfe with any sorrowes: for I goe to glorie, leauing you heere in a world of myserie, wherefore I would the howre were at hande to translate this Tragedie: then should I haue my wishe, and they suffice them with tyranny. But since it can not be so soone as I would, but perforce I shall stay tyll their lymitted leysure: I request you resolue your selfe of any

He sheweth the great courage of his Syster to the death.

doubt whatsoeuer, and arme your selfe to abide the bruntes of all theyr diuellishe deuises. Therefore prepare your selfe manfully, to taste of theyr tyranny, cast all your care on Christianitie: and the true God shall defend ye.

Mica Sheffola hearing the ioyful wordes of his Syster reioyced.

When I behelde my Syster, chaunged from care to courage, from mourning to myrth, and from pensiuenes to perfect gladnesse: what ioy I conceyued, is not nowe to be spoken of, for the wyllingnesse that she had to the death, caused me perfectly to beleeue, that their excessiue tormentes should not anoye and attaynt her: but that in the fulnesse of her fayth, she would withstand their practises whatsoeuer, and then I sayd vnto her.

The words he spake to his Sister.

Deere Syster, as I am right ioyfull of this your Christianlike courage: so wishe I you may remaine vnto the ende, but thus much comfort is sent you, and thus much good hope to harten you: that there is a Christian Champion in this Cittie, wyll aduenture lym and life in defence of your constancie, and thus much he hath wylled me to tell you, that this night you must passe in prayers, for his safe successe. Wherfore keepe this secrete to your selfe, for it is vnknowen to any, and least I should be in ought suspected: I wyll byd you adiew good Syster. With that the Iaylor came to attend our talke: and I seeing that departed. Then went I in to the *Soldanes* Armorie, and from thence brought the best defence I could finde, and heere is mine owne Sheeld, Launce and Courser: which I doubt not but wyll like you well.

⟨R⟩ Zelauto *hearing the discourse passed by* Mica Sheffola, *and hauing finished his Orisons: vnto him verie courteouslie replyeth in this manner.*

S IR, the good wyll I wishe you, and the dutifull courtesie I am ready to offer you, I trust shall suffice for to byd you good morrowe. These weapons which you haue brought, and this Armour heere present: shall (through the assistaunce of my God) eyther set at lybertie your godly Sister: or be bathed with my blood in the open feelde, for this I wyll assure you, and without vaunt be it spoken: I neuer in all my life went about any thing so wyllingly, as I nowe goe to the Combate for my conscience, and were he as great as *Goliah,* as stoute as *Sampson,* and as monstrous as the *Minotaures:* I wyll be so bolde as bestowe a fewe blowes, not doubting but they shall be indifferently delyuered, and that the *Soldane* him selfe shall say, he that wyll buye her better then I: is woorthy to haue her when he hath done.

And if afterwarde, by trayterous treason, he seeke to bereaue my life: yet shall he knowe, that no man deserueth it better then I. But I pray you (quoth I) doo you know the other Champion against whome I must wage battayle? is he any man of accoumpt, or of such estimation, as to fight in this quarrell taken in hand?

He aunswered me, that it was the *Soldanes* Sonne, named *Terolfo,* a man of synguler courage, and one that had aduentured verie woorthily in his tyme, bothe by Sea and Land, in verie great affayres.

Zelauto *after* Mica Sheffola *had ended his discourse: sayth vnto him.*

Zelauto *is armed with so good a courage, that hee doubteth not but to speede well.*

Terolfo *the* Soldanes *son, is he that must fyght against* Zelauto.

Mary all the better (quoth I) the more noble the man is: the more famous wyll the fight be, and ryght glad I am that it is the *Soldanes* Sonne: for then if I dye, I dye at the hands of a valiaunt Champion. And about what time thinke you (quoth I) that it wyll be when shee shall be conducted foorth to death?

Zelauto demaundeth at what tyme the Lady must suffer death.

Syr (quoth he) verie early, because they are verie wylling to dispatche her, least any other should seeme to take opinion of her fayth, and it wyll not be long nowe, for the Officers were gone to the prison to make her ready, and the Trumpet soundeth on the Castle, for any Champion that wyll come, the Stake is made ready to burne her at, and wood, and all thinges ready brought. The *Soldane* him selfe, and all his Lordes are ready, wherefore I knowe it wyll not be long hence now.

Well (sayd I) the time is welcome, whensoeuer it commeth, and if it shall please you to helpe to arme me: it shall not be long before I am ready too.

◀ Manniko Rigustello, *and* Dania

his wife commeth vp into the Chamber to Zelauto, *and there helpeth to arme him.*

The Hoste and his wife commeth vp to Zelauto.

THEN presently came vp mine Hoste and his Wife, who after they had courteouslie saluted me: they and the Gentleman, helped to arme me. After I was ready, I heard a great noyse of Trumpettes. Syr (quoth the Gentleman) nowe commeth this sorrowfull sight, heere commeth

the seelly Lambe lead vnto her slaughter. I looked
out, and there came the *Soldane* and his Lordes,
before him a great garde of Armed men, some on
horsebacke, some on foote, and next before the
Soldane, rode one on a verie gallant Steede, a valiaunt and comly Champion.

The order howe the
Lady was lead vnto
her death.

After the *Soldane* and his Lordes, came the innocent Lady, in a fayre whyte Roabe downe to the
ground, about her were the Tormenters, that
should payne her to death, then after them a company of auncient Matrones all in blacke, to
mourne the Ladyes death, and after them came all
the braue Ladyes and Gentlewomen of the Cittie,
all to see the execution of this poore innocent.

All these beeing past, the Gentleman tooke his
leaue of mee tyll I came to the place, which was
not farre of. Within a whyle I lystened, and heard
the Trumpette sounde verie shryll, then it stayed,
and sounded the second tyme, vp came mine
Hoste and sayde. Syr nowe it is tyme, hye you
quickly or else neuer.

The departure of
Mica Sheffola.

I got vp on Horsebacke, and by that tyme I was
come out of the doores, the Trumpet sounded
againe. Then rode I with all the possyble speede I
might, tyll I came to the place, and when the
Soldane and all his company sawe a defendour
come in such haste: they were all abashed. There
was great enquirie what I should be, and from
whence I came, the braue Ladyes and Damoselles,
they were exceeding ioyfull, and when I was entred the myddest, I saluted the *Soldane* as well as
I could, and lykewise the Champion, then made
I obeysaunce to all the company beside, who
thronged neere to heare what I would say, and
then began I to frame my talke in this order.

The comming of
Zelauto to the place
to fight for the Lady.

The woordes of Zelauto *to the* Sol-dane.

If right woorthy *Soldane,* and you also noble Lordes, by the verdict of your wisedomes, shall lycence mee to yeelde to lybertie, what I haue to saye, and be not offensiue at any thing heere spoken: I shall thinke you shewe mee nothing but Iustice and equitie, and then I shall accoumpt your Fame the more woorthy.

The Soldane *aunswereth* Zelauto.

Quoth the *Soldane,* thou hast free leaue to speake, and lybertie to doo what thou canst: but what wyll follow we can not assure thee. Why (quoth I) offering no iniurie to any person present, nor wishing to be no otherwise dealt with all, then my deedes deserue: I trust you shall finde no occasion of any offence, but that what I say, may be well borne with all. Well (quoth the *Soldane*) if all be well, it is the better for thee: if any thing yll, stand to your owne aduenture.

¶ Zelauto *beeing come to the place*
where he must defend the Ladyes cause, who stoode there
before him ready bound to a stake, and hauing
talked with the Soldane, *as touching pardon*
for his bolde attempt: thus beginneth
to make his Oration, in the
presence of them all.

Zelauto *nowe setteth a good face on the matter, not fearing the* Soldane.

AFTER I had well pondred the sharpe reply of the *Soldane,* and that since I was entred before them all, it behooued me to set a good face on the matter, and not dismay my self with any of their diuellish dealinges: neyther esteeming the furie of the *Soldane,* nor crauing the courtesie of any his companions: aduaunced my selfe for-warde, and sayd.

Since neyther promise may be proffered to pur-chase my pardon, nor licence for that I shall yeeld vnto lybertie: neither dismaying through doubt of your dealing, nor fearing the cheefest force of your furie, I pronounce in presence what my minde giues occasion: and wyll mayntaine the same with the losse of my life.

Beholde (inuincible *Soldane*) you noble Lords (and you renowned Matrones) a man, bothe dead and a lyue, a lyue to aduaunce the cause of this Lady: and dead in that my victory returneth losse of my lyfe. But yet remembring life is vncertayne, and death is so that each man may make accoumpt thereof: I nought esteeme the likelyhood of my life, but arme my selfe, as one willing to the death.

Zelauto *his Ora-tion.*

Yet by perfect proofe we see, that the tallest Tree, abydes many a bitter blaste, the brauest Bulwarke, by force is battered, the hautiest Hart, subiect to a fall, and the proudest person (at last) maketh his Cabben of clay: euen so your potencie may soone be peruerted, and the vttermost of your tyranny, cleane disapoynted. See heere the guyltlesse doomed to death, see heere the lewdest suffered to lyue, beholde where trueth is turnde out of all, see heere where falsehood boasteth in his brauerie.

But since rashnesse in speeche maketh me run too farre: the knowledge of my selfe calleth me backe againe, I confesse it is not my part to dis-alowe of your dealings, nor to contemne the prin-cipalitie, which now you professe: yet may I reprehend the abused aucthorytie, ruled by rigor and not by indifferencie. You will say, that

Princes are not to professe partialitie, and that the
Subiect should not meddle in the swaying of his
dignitie: yet ought the Prince to deale vprightly,
and not to pinche that partie, that auoucheth most
fayth and dutifull loyaltie. Admit that the Prince
may so farre ouer run him selfe, that by ambicious
heades, double dealers, and priuie enemies, he condempneth the man, that most dooth honour him:
yet is not his death to be prosecuted so hastily: but
to be considered of with wisdome and discretion.

This Lady for example, no straunger, but of
your owne blood, and no enimie to your Maiestie:
but rather one that wisheth you inestimable dignitie, she by you is condempned, for wishing you
well, and shee committed to this mortall death:
that seeketh to saue you from eternall death. What
heart so hard, can commit such crueltie? and what
beast so brutishe, but dealeth more naturally. If
to your owne blood, you will deale so tyrannically: how will you deale with me poore wretch
of so meane estimation? Me thinketh that though
the extremity you vse to the vttermost: Nature yet
should mooue with an inward affection, and
though that iustly she deserued the death: yet
should naturall kindnesse procure you to pittie.
Also among so many gallant youthes, none so
ventrous to defend her cause, nor none so in-
flamed with affection, as to mittigate her myserie.
Me thinke noble Ladyes, that some one of you
ought to haue stoode her defender: if no man had
the courage to hazard his lyfe. Admit that the estate of your Countrey consisted on this Ladyes
well fare: would you seeme so slouthfull, as to
suffer your whole Countrey to perishe, rather
then to make apparaunce of your manhood?

King *Codrus* beeing aduertised by the Oracle, that except he were slayne: his people should not vanquishe their enimies: armed him selfe lyke a Soldier, placing him selfe in the forefront of the armie, and there by his death, set all his people at quietnesse. Beholde what great affection was in this noble Prince, who more esteemed the sauegard and happy societie of his people: then his owne life.

Codrus *yeelded him selfe to dye for the sauegard of his people.*

Aglaurus, to shun the emminent daunger that was like to fall vpon *Athens*, seeing his death only might set it at liberty: threw him selfe headlong from the walles of *Athens*, and so ended the strife, where else it should haue bene conquered. But now attend you noble Ladyes, and you modest Matrones: let the excellent example of *Iphigenia* cause you to remember what care you ought to haue in the preuenting of such daungers as may happen, and by some one of you may be easily escaped. Shee (I say) seeing that her death would appease the rigor of her enimies, yeelded her selfe to be sacrificed. Oh admirable vertue, oh singuler constancie, her matche as rare to finde in these partes: as to see golden Goates to feede on greene mountaynes, yet wish I that all Women would prosecute her rare rule of life, and that some one *Iphigenia* among you, would hazard your hap to set free this Lady.

Aglaurus *by throwing himself from the walles of* Athens, *redeemed his Countrey.*

Iphigenia, *yeelded her selfe to be sacrificed.*

But least in wishing you to be warriours, I should seeme to shroude my selfe, and that you should thinke I come to prate, rather then to put my puissance in practise: I wyll cease to trouble you with ouermuch talke, and vtter the cause wherfore I come. First, I come to sue and intreate, if I may haue good successe, which is, that you would spare the life of this famous Lady: and not cut of her dayes in her gallantest prime, that you would remember the race shee is discended of: and woorke no wurse to her, then you would to your owne selues. Next, if your Lawes be so extreme that they may not spare punishment, and eke you your selues so wilfull, that you must needes woorke her wrack: I thinke it sufficient that you put her in exyle, with expresse charge in payne of death neuer to returne: so may your rigor be verie well asswaged, and shee for her paines indifferently penaunced. Thus in your Land shall you euer heereafter be magnified: and all people wyll laude your Princely dealinges. And lastly, if neyther of these peticions may seeme to take place, but that you must needes execute the vttermost of your crueltie: Heere am I by force of Armes to defend her quarrell, and against this your Champion will liue and dye in her defence. This is the cause of my comming, and this the dutie I haue to discharge.

The Soldane *stroken into a great quandarie.*

With that the *Soldane* began to looke on his Lords, and they on him, the Ladyes and all that were present, was stroken into a great maze, some for ioy clapped theyr handes, and some on the other side began to weepe: the poore distressed Lady stoode all this whyle bound to the stake, and the Tormentors ready to make the fire. At last the Champion began to come neerer vnto me: and the *Soldane* hauing taken good aduisement of my woordes, sayd as followeth.

❧ *The* Soldane *after he had well* *pondred the passed tale of* Zelauto: *made his reply in this order, as followeth.*

SIR, as we haue well aduised our selues of your woordes: so are we to giue aunswere, as wee shall thinke best, and as your talke seemeth to giue occasion. We are not to condempne you for that you haue spoken: nor yet to commend you, least you should receyue a priuate pride in your selfe, also your manhood we are not to reprooue, nor yet of your qualities we are not to accoumpt: although bothe of them in you haue made a seemely shewe, but as your manhood may misse, when you thinke most surest: so may your qualities be so craftie, as at last may deceyue your selfe. And where you haue alleaged, that naturall affection should woorke in vs, especially towards them of our owne Parentage: I aunswere, that were shee mine owne Childe, making an offence: shee is woorthy to be beaten, and so shee, altring from all her freends, Kinsfolke and faith: in our iudgementes shee is woorthy to taste the sharpest torments. Farder, you sayd that shee dooth it as an example in wishing our weale: we aunswere, That they which speak vs fayre and looue vs not: We will speake them as fayre, and trust them not, and shee that would take no warning when shee might, nowe if shee would, we will not accept of it. But belyke you are of the same opinion your selfe: and that makes you beare so much with her in that respect, if you be, choose you, the wurse will be your owne in the ende.

The Soldane *replieth to* Zelauto.

To rip vp the whole estate of your talke it were needelesse, and to trifle the time we doo not intend, our aunswer is this, neyther pittie shall procure vs to consider of her cause, nor exyle shall be graunted, to her for her offence: but only the death whereto shee is adiudged. Now win her and weare her, shewe the best of thy manhood: but take heede of the ende.

Zelauto *talketh to the Lady bound to the stake*.

When I perceyued the *Soldane* so fully bent, to bathe his handes in her guyltlesse blood, and that nothing but her death might seeme to suffice him: I went to the Lady, and thus I vsed my talke. Lady, neyther can I warrant you lyfe: or my selfe able to vanquishe your enimie, but how euer it be, of the death I doo assure my selfe, wherfore neither faint with feare, nor forgette your faith, but as you seeme to be constant vnto the death: so frame your peticions, the better shall I speede. If I redeeme you, it is the cheefest of my desire: if I dye my selfe, God will receyue my soule. Thus neyther trusting to the one, more then the other: or more accoumpting of lyfe, then I doo of death: I enter the feeld to fortifie your faith, and hazard my hap, as shall please God to speede me.

The Lady replyeth to Zelauto.

With that the Lady (whose comely and sweete countenaunce me thinkes I yet beholde) made aunswer vnto me as heere I shall tell you. Most noble Syr, I may thinke my selfe happy to haue so good a Champion: and coumpt the feelde wonne, how euer it speede: if you foyle my enemie, I haue that I looke for, yet if you dye your selfe: my state is farre wurse then it was before, rather had I to abyde the brunt, and you to sheelde your selfe: then to ende two bodies lyues, where one may suffise, so shall the enemie gorge him selfe with my blood: and your good wyll be neuerthelesse esteemed of. Therefore good Syr, content you, and escape hence if you can, for I am prepared to abide what it shall please them to lay on me.

Nowe credit me Syr, these her woordes dyd so greatly encourage me: that had it beene against Men and Monsters, yea, the furious feendes, I would haue ventured what euer had betyde me: So then I sayd vnto her. No Lady, what I haue promised, shall be presently performed, they shall not say, that a Christian will eate his woorde: but that he dare venture against the proudest of them. And so fare well good Lady, for heere goes your woorthy Knight, who before hee returneth, wyll eyther subdue thy enimie: or loose his lyfe in the feelde.

Zelauto speaketh againe to the Lady.

When the Champion sawe I was returned: he came vnto me saying. Syr, as you are a Knight at Armes, and heere professe the same: so nowe according to the order and custome of the Lawe, I am to desire your name.

Terolfo the Soldanes sonne speaketh to Zelauto.

Trueth Syr (quoth I) and of my name I am not ashamed, my name is *Zelauto,* and I come to maintaine the cause of this Lady. Nowe am I to request as much of you.

Zelauto his replye.

Syr (quoth he) my name is *Terolfo,* I am sonne to the *Soldane,* and heere am chalenger, on the behalfe of my Father. I trust you wyll pardon what shall passe betweene vs heere in this place.

Terolfo his reply.

With all my heart (quoth I) and I am not in doubt, but you will doo the like, for if I am ordayned to dye in this place: I frankly and freely forgiue him that dooth the deede, so it be but one man.

Zelauto forgiueth Terolfo.

Terolfo *forgiueth* Zelauto.

And if you Syr (quoth he) are the man to dispatch my dayes: with all my heart I forgiue you my death.

Then were the Coursers sent abroade to make roome, the men appoynted to iudge the fyght, euerie thing in order appoynted, that belongeth to the matter, we went about, hee fetching his course one way, and I an other, and so we began a fierce and terrible fight.

❧ *Then began a valiant and fierce*
Combat, between Zelauto, *and the* Soldanes *sonne* Terolfo, *which was so excellently well handled on bothe sides: that it was doubtfull to whome the victorie should fall, but yet at the last, after many fierce assaults,* Zelauto *kylleth him in the open feeld, and so redeemed the Lady from death, and what happened to him afterward.*

WE ENDVRED so long in daungerous and doubtfull fight, that he had small hope to vaunt of any victorie, or I any likelyhood to boast of the bargaine, but credite me, he for his part verie valiantly behaued him selfe, and deserued rightly to be well esteemed of, for neyther any feare could inforce him to faynt: nor wearinesse of warre cause him leaue of, but stoutly and couragiouslie, behaued him selfe manfully.

At last, it was my fortune to strike the stroke that dispatched him, the which was as great a greefe vnto me: as to any of his familiar freendes, for gladly would I haue conquered him, and saued his lyfe: but not bothe vanquish him, and bereaue his life. But as you know your selfe, a man in such affayres, dealeth as best he can, for the sauegarde of him selfe, is his cheefest desire: euen so I was warie least the lot should haue lyghted on me, and so valiantly slew him before his father and all his freendes.

Zelauto killeth Terolfo in fight.

But to see what leaping, what clapping of handes, what throwing vp of Cappes, and what great ioy was made of the Ladyes and the common people, would haue reioyced you to heare. Then was the Lady let loose, and I commaunded to come before the *Soldane*, who was not before so willing to the death of the Lady: as he was now sorrowfull for the yll successe of his sonne.

The Ladyes and common people reioyce at the victorie of Zelauto.

When I was come before him, he sayd. We confesse (Syr Knight) that you haue done the deede manfully, and that you are woorthy a greater rewarde, then heere you are lyke to gayne: but yet since you haue bereaued my Sonne of life, we must therefore deale the more hardly with you. And as the reward you must haue for your victorie, is death: euen so we wyll you to take it patiently, and not to striue, least farder harme doo arise vnto you.

The woordes of the Soldane to Zelauto.

If you had saued the life of my sonne: we could then haue permitted more pittie, then nowe we can, or if you had wounded him, yet that he might haue lyued: your freedome had beene sooner bought, where now all the ritches of *India* is not able to doo it. Your selfe was not altogether

ignoraunt before, how that the redeeming of her
life: was the death of the partie whatsoeuer, and
we infourmed you, that in such sort you might
behaue your self, as no man should molest you,
you haue now dealt so with vs, that no freendship
may be found, and beside, your Christianitie dooth
vtterly condempne you. Yet wyll we somewhat
vse you honestly in the matter, you shall not
presently feele the terror of your paine: but for
the space of fowre dayes, lyfe shall be graunted
you, in which tyme, dispose your selfe to dye,
for there is no other meanes can be made for you.
Thus doo we not deale with you as sharply as we
might: nor vse you otherwise then the Lawe was
appointed, she hath her life, let her goe where she
please: and you your death, which we are sorie
for, yet can not it be holpen.

When I had well aduised my selfe of this sharpe
sentence, and that no remedy there was, but Lawe
must proceede, then looking on all sides, and beholding the trickling teares of the modest Matrones, the Ladyes and Gentlewomen all to lament
for me, the common people also vsing such pittifull cryes, that it greeued them intierly to heare
such wofull newes: taking heart couragiously, and
dreading no myserie, but trusted in my Christe
assuredlie: and thus I aunswered the *Soldane*.

*The woordes of Ze-
lauto to the* Soldane.

Renowned *Soldane*, if neyther the valure of the
deede that is done, nor the mestiue mones of these
sorrowfull mourners, is of sufficiencie to procure
me your pittie, but that I must needes abide the
death, and there is no remedie: then beholde me
as wylling to the losse of my lyfe, as I was dillygent to discharge the Ladyes distresse. It is not my
lyfe that I doo accoumpt of, nor yet my death
that wyll returne your aduauntage: This Ladyes

well fare is all my desire, and my dying for her,
to cause you worke no more iniurie to her.

But since the death of your Sonne is the cause
of your choller, and that if he had lyued, the better might haue beene my happe: I trust you are
not ignoraunt what belongeth to the Lawe of
Armes, and what passeth betweene vs in fight
ought to be pardoned. I was as vnsure of my lyfe
as he, and I was as hopefull of victorie as he: If
then bothe parties doo their dillygence as beseemeth them, what harme eyther of them sustayne is not to be accoumpted of. Therfore if for
his death you deale with me extremely: I must
needes say you vse extremitie, and no Lawe or
Iustice.

And for the fowre dayes of respyte you haue
graunted, I am to thanke you, for that it is more
of your clemencie: then of my simple deseruing,
yet in the meane tyme I accoumpt my selfe but a
dead man, for that your doome is passed, albeit
Lawe is to execute.

Wherefore, you noble Ladyes, you vertuous
Damoselles, and you deere Lady, in whose defence my death is obtayned, from my heart I bid
you all farewell, wishing as wel to your sweete
selues, as to mine owne poore heart, and if my
tyme had not beene cut of so soone as nowe it
is: you should haue seene that which now I am
not able to vnfolde. In your causes I lyue and dye,
and for your sakes I haue thus much attempted,
therefore to you all I byd farewell. And to you all
in generall, whose wylles I see should not want to
woorke my well fare, I would my abilytie were as
sufficient to pleasure you: as I would be wylling
with my paynes to profite you.

Then the *Soldane* and all his trayne departed,

*Zelauto giueth his
fare well to all the
Ladyes and Gentle-
women.*

Zelauto *and his Hoste were lead to prison.*

and I was conducted with a dozen Officers, with their Halberds to my lodging, where when I was vnarmed: both mine Hoste and I were lead to the prison, such a multitude of people following vs, and such good report euerie one gaue me: that credite me, I went as wylling to the prison, as to my lodging.

Mica Sheffola *awayted for* Zelauto *at the prison.*

At the prison gate I saw *Mica Sheffola* (the Ladyes Brother, for whome I aduentured) awayting my comming, who had prouided for me, the best and pleasauntest Chamber in the prison, and got me the lybertie of the Garden, to walke at my pleasure, and at last rounded me in the eare saying. Good Syr, feare no daunger, for God and I will

The Hoste apprehended and must dye.

hence delyuer you, but I am sorie for your Hoste, because he is already apprehended vnto the *Soldane,* and his Maiestie tolde vnto me euen now when I departed from him: that to morrowe he shall be executed before the prison. I dare tarie no longer for feare of beeing suspected, I haue prouided all thinges for you heere, and to morrowe I will come againe, about the howre he must dye.

Alas me thought these were farre wursser newes, then the other, I could not speake to mine Hoste, because he was haled and pulled in so violently, and layde in a deepe dungeon by himself, and clogged with so many Irons, as he could possibly beare.

The Hostesse commeth to the prison to Zelauto.

Well, in the after noone, my Hostesse *Dania* came to speake with her Husbande, but could not, then came shee vp to me, informing me of all that *Mica Sheffola* had tolde me. I demaunded of her, how he was knowen? She aunswered, that for the woordes hee vsed in my cause, and other suspicious talke. Well (quoth I) you were not best to

tarie heere long, least you be suspected likewise.
No Syr (quoth shee) I wyll byd you fare well
tyll to morrowe, and then shall you see my poore
Husband miserably martyred.

In the morning returned *Mica Sheffola*, bringing me a great deale of Golde to spende in the
prison, and demaunded of me, how I was vsed in
the prison? I aunswered, very well I thanked him,
for his sake I wanted nothing. Then he desyred
the Iaylor to let me into a Chamber towarde the
streete, that I might see mine Hoste put to death,
the which I thanke him he dyd.

Then (quoth he vnto me) without the Cittie, I
haue prouided for you a lustie Courser, and Armour to defende you withall, soone at mydnight,
at the dead tyme of the nyght, shall you be let into
the Garden, and there clymbe ouer to me, and I
will receyue you, for I haue gotten the keyes of
the *Soldanes* Treasurie, and soone at mydnight
will I steale from thence so much as shall serue you
in your trauayle: A deere freende of mine, and
one as good a Christian as my selfe shall goe with
you, to conduct you on your way from all your
enimies, thus will I fulfill my promise vnto you,
and yet not woorke my selfe any discredite: so
that you be ready at the howre appoynted, for
the Iaylors Wife wyll let you into the Garden, and
so on the backe syde of the Cittie you shall escape
away safely. Then a mightie hole shall be broken
in your Chamber, as though you had stollen out
into the streete: I dare tarie no longer, remember
your selfe soone, and so God be with you.

Nowe surely me thought it was the greatest
freendshippe that euer I found at any mans handes
in all my lyfe, especially, I beeing a prisoner, and

Mica Sheffola
*returneth in the morn-
ing.*

*An notable deuise to
helpe* Zelauto *out of
prison.*

hee to defraude his owne Vnckle in such sort to pleasure me with all.

The Hoste brought foorth to death.

Well, at lengthe my Hoste *Manniko Rigustello*, was brought out in his shyrt, and such a multitude of people was there to see him: as was the other day to see the Lady. Then went he vp vppon the Scaffolde, where they would not suffer him to speake, but presently layde him vppon an Ingine that they had made: and so wrested him to death, verie cruellie and tyrannicallie.

When he was dead, one member of him was throwen this way, an other that way, so that all his members was dispersed about the streetes, a verie greeuous and dolefull syght to see. Thus was my poore Hoste martyred and mangled, and I remayned in great sorrow to thinke therupon.

❧ The Gentlewoman of the Prison

came vp to Zelauto, *and to expell the thoughtes that troubled his minde: conducted him into the Garden, and shewed him the Monuments of* Brisaro de Saroto, *who sometime was conquerour of that Cittie.*

Oriana *the Mistresse of the prison came vp to* Zelauto.

REMAYNING in these pensiue plightes, yet greatly encouraged through the comfort that *Mica Sheffola* gaue me: at last came vp into my Chamber the Gentlemans wife, who kept the prison, beeing named *Oriana*, a verie gallant and courteous Gentlewoman, who in the *Italian* language, thus saluted me. *Ditemi per cortesia Gen-*

tilhuomo, come sta vostra S.? I aunswered.
Carrissima mia Signora, sto bene, sempre al com-
mando vostro, e vi rendo mille gratie. After much
conference passed betweene vs together (quoth
shee) shall it lyke you so well Gentleman, as to
walke with me into the Garden.

Gentlewoman (quoth I) if I would deny so
small a request: I were to be accoumpted verie
vncourteous. Not so (quoth shee) for perhappes
other occasions may so hinder you: that you haue
not the leysure which I seeme to require, and then
I might be accoumpted more carelesse then cyrcumspect, in entring so rashlie to perturbe your
patience. You doo well good Gentlewoman
(quoth I) to frame your selfe so faultie: else
should not I haue knowen howe to accuse my
selfe.

Well, we walked into the Garden, where shee
gaue me to vnderstande of that which *Mica Shef-*
fola had tolde me, and that shee at the myddle of
the night, would conuey me into the Garden, and
so ouer the wall to him. I gaue her great thankes
for her courtesie, as it dyd cheefly behooue me.
At last, shee opened a great doore, where as we
entred into a verie fayre Hall, and there was the
Monuments of a notable Champion.

Loe Syr (quoth shee) the redoubted Monuments of *Brisaro de Saroto*, who conquered this
Cittie eleuen tymes, and framed the good orders, that now heere are vsed. Gentlewoman
(quoth I) it seemeth that he hath been a noble
Champion, and I thanke you hartily for making
me pertaker of the sight therof. With other familiar talke we passed out the time tyll supper,
then went I to supper, and afterward I layd me

Oriana *telleth*
Zelauto, *how at night*
shee wyll conuey him
ouer the garden wall.

Shee sheweth him the
Monumentes of
Brisaro de Saroto.

Shee commeth vp bydding him to prepare him selfe.

downe vpon my bed. About the thyrd howre of the night, came shee vp, and tolde me that *Mica Sheffola* had entred into her Garden with a great deale of Treasure, and there he had left it, desiring me to prouide my selfe within an howre.

I thanked her hartily, and tolde her, I would be as ready when she came to fetche me: as she was wylling to come for me. I could not lay mine eyes together for the ioy I conceyued, to thinke how God had blessed me, in sending me such freendes among all mine enimies.

Within an howre after, she came vp very softly againe, saying: Come away Syr, your freend taryeth your comming. It was no neede to byd me make haste, considering I should escape so harde a plunge.

¶ Zelauto *with* Oriana *the Mistresse*

of the prison went downe into the Garden, at the myddle of the night, and was conueyed ouer to Mica Sheffola, *and so escapeth from his enimies.*

WHEN I was come downe into the Garden, finding a Ladder ready set for me to clymbe ouer: I tooke leaue of the Gentlewoman, and so went ouer the wall, there stoode *Mica Sheffola* at hand to receyue me. Quoth he, for the looue of God let vs make all haste possible, for the Trumpettes hath sounded the thyrde watche, and now wyll they come without the Cittie: and if we speede not the faster, we are lyke to be taken.

Zelauto goeth with Mica Sheffola away.

We trudged apace tyll we came out of all daun-

ger, and at last we came where one heelde a lusty
Courser for me, and Armour lay ready for me to
put on, and a lyttle before was a Companion for
me, who awayted the comming of any body, to
giue vs warning thereof. When I was Armed and
vppon Horsebacke (quoth he) though I haue not
recompenced with as much as I would: yet haue
I done what possible I might: there is one before
shall lyue and dye with you, he wyll conduct you
toward *Constantinople.* Thus wylling to preuent
all daungers that may happen, and wyshing you
prosperitie in all your affayres: a short fare well
shall suffise, and so to God I commend you.

Well Syr (quoth I) I will not trifle out the time
with long and tedious thankes, I am bound to pray
for you, commend me to mine Hostesse *Dania,*
and to the good Gentlewoman *Oriana,* that conueyed me ouer the wall, and so we bothe parted.

Zelauto departeth from Mica Sheffola.

Within a whyle I ouer tooke my Companion,
who was as honest, vertuous and ciuill a Gentleman as euer I rode with all in my lyfe. Hee and I
rode together toward *Constantinople,* in which
iourney befell diuers other accidentes. Thus haue
you heard my first aduentures in *Persia:* now tell
me your iudgement thereof.

Astræpho.

My iudgement is too slender in such a myraculous matter, but sure you haue had the best Fortune that euer I heard any, so neare the death: and
yet to be delyuered, now credite me it is excellent.
Well, now will I goe to get our Dinner, and will
leaue you heere tyll I come agayne, in which tyme
you shall peruse a proper Deuise that I will shew
you. How say you, are you contented?

Astræpho *giueth his censure on this passed tale, and goeth to prouide dinner.*

Zelauto.

Syr, right ioyfull of your courtesie, also glad to accept your offer, and after Dinner we will discourse of the rest, if you please.

Astræpho.

With all my heart Syr, wherefore come in and I wyll giue it you, I beleeue you wyll lyke well of it after you haue read it.

FINIS.

The Author.

Courteous Gentlemen, in the meane tyme as Astræpho is prouiding his Dinner, and hath left Zelauto at home to peruse at his pleasure on an Amorous discourse: I wyll seeme so sausie, as to molest his studies, and desire him to let you be partakers of this Delycate discourse. I hope I shall not neede to be all day in crauing: nor he so vncourteous to deny my request, if he should, I must confesse he offereth me great iniurie, in taking so much paines for him: I deserue to craue a mightier matter. Well, I will assure my selfe to speede in my purpose, and you shall haue the hearing of the Dayntie Deuise. If after you haue read it, you finde it woorth his hyre, and that it hath pleased you, which is my whole wishe: I shall then prouide a Peach for all prating Parasites: and keepe a sweete Figge to gratifie my freend with all.

Honos alit Artes.

FINIS.   *A. Munday.*

Astræpho.

A Delycate Deuise by him delyuered
to Zelauto, *wherein is gallantly discoursed,*
the Amorous lyfe of a Scholler, and the braue behauiour
of a martiall Gentleman, the one at last by looue
aswell conuinced: as the other, who alway
professed him selfe a Subiect to the
same: neyther friuolous nor fan-
tasticall, but delyghtfull,
and to no man
preiudiciall.

The thyrd part of the
Fountayne of Fame.

Written by the sayd Author A. M.
Seruaunt to the right Honorable, the Earle of Oxen-
forde.

Honos alit Artes.

The Author, to the curteous
Readers.

GENTLEMEN (and ryght courteous whatsoeuer) I must needes confesse, that the
painfull Pylgrimage of Zelauto, hath beene so tedious vnto you in the perusing, that neither could
you gaine any delight in the discourses: nor such
methode of matter as you looked for, but euen
playne Dunstable way, he hath tolde you an olde
Canterburie tale. Yet on your iudgementes I am
not to define, for that they are diuers: nor to suppose you will lyke, without I were better assured, for the one may shew the rashnesse of a
vainglorious head: and the other a presumption to
conster any mans behauiour. Antisthenes sayth,
that as of the Serpent, the Phisition receyueth part
of his remedies: so the wise man of his verie enimies (contrarie to expectation) shall obtayne some
profite. Diogenes beeing by a malicious and spitefull tongue, reprehended of a fault long before
committed: made aunswere. I remember the time
when I was such a one as thou art now: but such
an one as I am now wilt thou neuer be.

Likewise Gentlemen, ambicious heads, are apt
to send foorth spitefull speeches, and if they can
possyble catche a hole in a mans coate: the same
wyll they lay euerie day in his dishe: But such
secrete Serpentes in bewraying their behauiour,
can not hurt him whome they wyllingly would:
but confound them in their craftyest inuentions.

Aristotle sayth, that he which receyueth a false peece of coyne, dooth but sustayne a reasonable losse: but he that trusteth a fayned freend in steede of a true, may endammage him selfe to his vtter vndooing, few such freends God send me: and as much good money as shall please him. But now in the meane while Gentlemen, whyle such coyne may be currant, and such freendes found: I sende you Astræphos delycate discourse, to make mery with the bad banquet you haue had. And though I haue no Cumfettes and Carawayes to bestowe vppon you: iudge my good will is neuer-thelesse, if might could mayntayne it. Thus of a little take a little when you come thereto: and of a little leaue a little how euer you doo.

FINIS.

Yours to vse to his power.
A. Munday.

❡ *The Amorous lyfe of* Strabino *a*

Scholler, the braue behauiour of Rodolfo *a martiall*
Gentleman, and the right reward of
Signor Truculento *a*
Vsurer.

Cap. 1.

THE RECORDES of auncient antiquitie,
vnfoldeth in apert, and liuely manner the
happy and prosperous estate, of the florishing and
famous Cittie *Verona*, whose *Accademies* so
woorthily gouerned, and the Schollers so effectually instructed: that it caused Syr *Vincentio* of
Pescara, to sende his sonne *Strabino*, there to be
trayned vp in such vertuous educations: as was
meete for one of his tender time. This *Strabino*,
a gallant and lusty youth, of forme well featured,
of audacitie expert, in manners well nurtured, but
from Martiall affayres wholy enclined, and to
looue one seuerely enthraled: fel at length in ac-
quayntaunce with one *Rodolfo*, a Gentlemans
sonne of the Cittie, who more vsed the Schole for
his pleasure, then any profite, more for a pastime
to talke and conferre with his freendes: then for
any minde he bare to his booke. And this *Rodolfo*
was one that greatly gaue himselfe to Martiall exercises, a disdayner of looue, and a reiecter of the
company of Women. Betweene these twayne
were ioyned such a league of Amytie: that neyther bitter blastes should procure the breach

thereof, nor any accident whatsoeuer, mooue them to mislike one of the other, but euen brotherlyke were vnited, tyll terme of lyfe were vtterly expired. *Strabino* vsually frequenting the house of his freend and brother *Rodolfo*, who had a Sister in all poynts so well proportioned: that the lookes of her Amorous countenaunce, infected in the heart of *Strabino*, such a restlesse rage, a torting torment, a Feuer so fantasticall: that none but only shee must be the curer thereof. Now are his bookes reiected, and his fancie followed: his study banished, and the Gentlewoman dutifully serued. Who (alas) although he were her superior: of her was regarded, as her farre inferior. He lykes, he looues, he sues, he serues, he runnes, he waytes: she lowres, she frownes, she disdaynes, and vtterly reiecteth his company. Which when he sawe, that his proffered paynes were esteemed as trifles, his continuall courtesie, regarded as lyght as a feather, and his affectioned seruice, cleane cast out of memorie: walked into the feeldes, and thus discoursed with him selfe.

Alas *Strabino*, yll hap hadst thou to lyght on this lucklesse lot, to looue where thou art disliked, to serue, where thou art nothing regarded, and to fancie where looue is extinguished. What mooued thee to make her thy Goddesse that regardeth thy paines as light as a May game? What mooued thee to make her thy Mistresse: who scorneth the good will of so trusty a seruant? What, is there no more Women in the world but one? Is there none can please thee so much as she? Art thou framed of such ylfauored mettall, that all will mislyke thee? In *Pescara* thou barest the cheefest prayse: in *Verona* thou art nothing esteemed of.

In *Pescara* thou wast looued, in *Verona* thou art reiected: but alas I remember, who trusteth to a Womans will, were as good leane on a broken staffe, for when she pleaseth, then she looueth: and when she is displeased, she hateth like a Tode, therfore well maist thou remooue thy fancy: and set as light by her, as she dooth by thee. But alas *Strabino*, if thy deedes might aunswere to thy woordes, then there were some hope of health: but thou art so surely tied, that vnpossible were it for thee to get loose when thou pleaseth, thou sayst thou wilt doo this and that, but alas, if thou couldest, thou wouldest, therfore neuer speake against thy conscience, for that were no credit. I looue her so intierly, that I can not refraine me: I fancie so forcibly, that I cannot remooue me. She is the Saint whome I serue, she is the Goddesse whome I adore, and she it is must ease my payne, else shall I neuer be holpen. Thou hast not yet tried her: therfore neuer speake the wurst of her, though thou hast showen thy selfe by sundry signes: yet canst thou not say she refuseth thee, because thou hast not opened the state wherin thy well fare standeth. Thou art to blame to vse these woords against her that neuer offended thee, and thou deseruest small courtesie, for thy so rash iudgement. She is syster to thy freend: he is gentle of nature, so may she be: he is courteous in con-ference, so may she be: he looues thee well, so may she do, therfore neuer conster things at the wurst, before thou haue occasion. Thinkest thou she knoweth the secretes of thy heart, that neuer talked with her? How were it possible she should looue thee, when she knoweth not whether thou looouest her or no? Perswade thy selfe to speede of thy purpose, faynt heart neuer wan fayre Lady, and a halfe hearted Soldier is terrified at the first allarum: fyrst prooue her, then prayse her, when thou hast tryed, then thou mayst trust: hye thee home in hope, and finding her at conuenient leysure, shew her thy sute. Thus the poore oppressed *Strabino* returned to the Mansion of his Mistresse, and finding her sitting at her Sampler in the garden: he tooke heart a fresh, and went and sate down by her, framing such deuises, as she might haue occasion to speake vnto him, who when she saw how merily disposed he was, sayd. Surely syr *Strabino*, I haue wanted your company all this day, for I haue sitten heere very solitary, and lackt such company as might procure some pleasure, and now you are come: I hope we shall passe the time more merier, then hytherto I haue done, and therfore you are welcome hartily.

Strabino hearing the courteous words of his Lady *Cornelia:* was surprised with such inward ioy, that he neyther minded his former feare, nor yet the present peryll that might happen to him, but wholy depending vpon his dutifull alleageaunce, and imbracing in minde and thought her supposed lyking: hazardeth his heart to stand vnto the hap, and yeeldeth him conquered wholy to her clemencie. Wherfore, he neyther distracting his sences with any seuerall motion, nor occupying his brayne vpon manifolde matters: desyreth pardon for that which his lyppes shall yeelde vnto lybertie, and her good construction in his actions whatsoeuer.

Syr (quoth she) if we talke of familliarity, perforce I must vse you freendly: if vpon nouelles, I will handle you as nicely: if vpon present proofe,

I will vse you pleasauntly: if vpon all, I will accoumpt you as a merie companion, so that looke
what is spoken in decent or honest wise: doubt
you not but it shall be as honestly entertained,
therfore say as pleaseth you.

¶ Strabino, *and* Cornelia, *courteous-*
ly conferreth together.

Cap. 2.

LADY (quoth *Strabino*) I muse why the Gods,
framing you first to be as a comfortable companion vnto man: you should so much digresse as
to be the only instrument of our sorrowfull sadnesse, rather a woorker of our woe: then one
that wisheth our well fare. For this is perfectly
knowen (I speake not vpon had Iwist) that you
Women, for the most part, are so coy of your
conditions, and so curious in your conceytes: that
you neyther esteeme the quantitie nor quallitie of
affection: nor yet the only perfect ground of our
prosperity. For admit that a whyle you beare vs
in hand with many an Amorous countenaunce,
many a gallant glose of firme fayth and fidelitie,
yea, many a subtill surmise of pure looue and affection, haue you once gotten that which you
would haue, to fleece our purses to pranke you in
pride, that you may sweat in your Sylks, whyle
we goe threadbare, you on your Pantofles, when
we haue scant a good shooe to our foote, you at
your delycate iunckets, when we are glad to ryse
with emptie bellyes, and you so much in your

brauerie, that you bring vs to vtter beggerie: In fayth, then fare well frost, more such haue we lost.

Nay now, since he can holde out no longer: fare well he, in faith he was a good fellowe whyle he had it, but nowe since he hath no more inke in his pen: let him goe shake his eares, a new customer, a new. So long time was he fed with fancies: that after he cursseth his folly. So long looued in lookes: that at length he lamenteth his losse. So long helde vp with wanton and wily woordes: that in the ende he cursseth such paltrie fables. A colde sute, and a harde penniwoorth haue all they that traffique for such merchandize. On the other side, let a man holde vp you at rack staues, diferre you of with doubtfull delayes, alleadge vnto you many defectes of abillitie, and besides that, keepe that from you which most willingly you would haue: In faith, then he is a counterfayt cranke, a shamlesse sheepbyter, a worldly miser, he is no good fellowe, that will not lay his penny by theyrs, a craking Companion, an eue dropper: with such and so many floutes they haue, that it is woonderfull to heare.

What great reproche is this to such wanton Women, that regard more an ell of pleasure, then an ynch of profite? more desirous of loathsome lybertie, then they care for contented lyuing? What maketh so many young Gentlemen crack theyr credite, loose theyr good name, mortgage theyr lyuinges, barter away all they haue: but such carelesse company? When before, they were in good and honest commendation among all men: now are they glad to hide theyr heads for shame.

I speake not this (deere Lady) to the reproche

of all Women: for that were meere impudencie:
but I speake in the contempt of all such as dayly
frequent it, as these Cortizans which abide in the
brothell house heere in *Verona*, and besides them,
many a one that beares a gallant grace through
the Cittie: taketh a snatch now and then, which
by right deserue a greater reproche, then they that
so dayly vse it. For by such meanes is vice in-
truded among the vertuous, making many that
(God knowes) are well disposed lyuers, to be
lyghtly accoumpted of, only by vsing the company of such carelesse creatures.

Syr *Strabino* (quoth *Cornelia*) your discourse
hath beene delyghtfull, yet sauoureth it sharpe
some where, belyke you haue bene bitten, or
stung by some of these Waspes: and that maketh
you so expert in bewraying theyr qualities, for the
mother would neuer haue sought her daughter
in the Ouen, but that shee had beene there her
selfe, and he that is galded, hath good occasion to
kicke. You haue beene bartering, and found all
so deere in the market: that no butter wyll sticke
on your bread, or belyke you haue sauced some
body: and payd sweetly for it.

But what maketh you to exclayme against
women in this order? haue you looued, and not
beene looued againe? haue you sought for honny,
and caught the Bee by the tayle: or haue you neuer
looued, and wholy giuen your selfe there against?
if so you haue, the harder is your happe, for farre
vnable are you to stand against the decree of the
gods, and haue you not read of diuers that haue
repugned against looue: which haue beene in-
forced to fancie theyr inferiors? Take heede *Strabino*, least in your denying to looue some gallant

Lady: you be not procured to fancie som poore *Fachine* heere in *Verona*. If you haue looued, and not beene looued againe: you are to mooue your sute, and if it be to such a one who is free from all other, and may well be your match: there is no doubt but after many sharpe showers, a gallant gale of winde will blow in the Skie, that will send your ioyes on heapes to you. I giue you the best counsayle that I can, and I would my proffered paynes any way might pleasure you. If either my woorde, counsayle, credite, or ought else may preuayle you to her whome you lyke: credite me, you shall not finde me so ready in promising, as I wyll be in the performaunce therof.

Now Gentlemen, iudge you what sundrie and seuerall quandaries assayled the assaulted minde of poore *Strabino*, to heare such courteous talke pronounced by the person whome hee most honored and obeyed. Yet doubted he, that if shee knew the very originall and only helpe for his heauines: shee would be as slowe to performe, as she was ready to promise, but yet buylding still on good hope of her bountie: hee proceeded into farder talke.

My hope is (quoth he) my good Lady and Mistresse, that what hath passed in my presumptuous talke, you will conster it at the best: but sure as yet I am free from that which you haue supposed, only this I am to confesse, that I loue and lyke, where I am neither refused nor yet entertained, wherfore I can not condempne vpon no occasion: nor I can not prayse before it be deserued. So that I am neither to vaunt as victor: nor yet to yeeld as altogether conquered. And why I haue enuyed against these sort of Women, I can yeeld you some sufficient reason: I haue known diuers of my

freends, that haue wasted out theyr web of youthfull time, in frequenting company with such wilfull Women. As for example, one deere freende
of mine, who was tost, turmoyled, and vtterly
made hauock of: among those whome he thought
had looued him deerest, yea some that were of
good name and credit, that sucked him drye: and
then matched them selues with other. Therfore I
say, it is hard to know who a man may trust now
a dayes: for you Women are so craftie, that a man
cannot tell howe to deale with you.

In deede Syr (quoth she) though we be craftie,
you men are more deceyptfull. It behooueth vs to
stand vpon our reputation, and to make the matter nice and coy to some, for when they haue once
caught vs: they will vse vs as they lyst. What sorrowe and care is it to be a maried Wife? that
which God hath ordayned to be a comfort and
solace betweene man and woman, is made nowe a
thing of most contempt: for when we be maried,
then commeth our cares all at once: how many
frowning lookes? how many crabbed counte-
nances? how many sharpe woordes? beside, how
many continuall greefes and sorrowes of the
minde? If our Husbandes be a lyttle displeased:
all the house must be out of quiet. If he frowne,
then what is next hand, flyes at the face of his
Wife. If he see her but merily disposed in any company, then is he ielous: if she looke on any man,
then she lusteth after him. Then is she watcht and
spied, in euery place where she goeth, to catche
her in a tryp, the which vrgeth her sooner to doo
it, when before she neuer thought it. What terror,
and what diuellish mindes are these of men: who
when they come to wooing, then plead they sim-

plicitie: then yea forsoothe, and no forsoothe, this
shall be and that shall be, when God knowes,
when it comes to perfection: it is neyther so, nor
so.

Can you blame Women, if they be so lothe to
graunt to your requestes? and can you thinke
them so harde, when you your selues are harder
then the Adamant? Can you say Women are ordayned as a plague vnto men: when as you your
selues plague them so cruelly? O deepe dissem-
blers, O prating Parasites? What subtill Sophis-
ters? What faire mouthed fellowes are these?
What paynted sheathes, fayre without and fowle
within? Who would thinke that you could beare
such a double heart about with you. I hope you
shall be fayne to say at length, *Ars deluditur arte*.
Hencefoorth therefore neuer enuy at Women:
when you are wurse your selues, nor neuer play
the Crauens, as Cockes of your owne dunghyll:
the shame wyll redound where it is woorthy, and
you shall be forced to crye *Peccaui*. Ah Syrra,
though you haue all the learning, God hath leant
vs some wyt, that wee should not be to much
deceyued. Therefore neuer vpbrayde vs with such
Rhetorical gloses, nor neuer fall out with those
who are your best freendes: If you lyke vs, loue
vs: if not, let vs alone.

Strabino, halfe driuen in feare of incurring his
Ladyes displeasure, and doubting least his talke
had bread some cause of melancholie: calles vp
his wittes together, to make amends for his former
fault. For thought he, if now I comming to speake
for mine owne auayle, and to gayne the good wyll
of my best belooued, should seeme to apprehend
or reprehend in such causes as willingly shee

would not: it might marre all my matter, and throwe all my good Fortune into the fyre. Wherfore, euen as the childe when he hath made a fault, commeth creeping on his knees with bytter teares, willing to kisse the rod, and so to pacifie the yre of his Parents whome he displeased, or as the Ape when he hath nipt one to the quick, and seeeth the whip holden vp in signe of correction: commeth with chattering the teethe, holding vp the ten bones, so to content his maisters displeasure conceyued: Even so meekely and mildly commeth *Strabino* to the loouing lap of his Lady, and in sygne and token of humilitie, vttereth these woordes. Deere Lady and Mistresse, not so wel satisfied and contented with your reasonable replie: as sorrowfull for suffering my tongue so rashly to offend you. Rather impute it therefore to obliuiousnesse of my selfe: then to any willingnesse to incurre your anger. More honour trulie shall it be to you, quietly to put vp the chollorike woords of an impudent Scholler: then to menace your anger, where as sorrow sufficient is retayned. It is a good Horse that neuer stumbleth, he is verie cyrcumspect that speaketh alway without a fault, and he is verie vpright that neuer committeth crime. I must confesse my tongue ran before my wyt, and my mouth vttered that which my heart neuer thought. But the best is, my boasting brauerie, can blemishe none of your bountie: nor my franticke foolishnesse, impayre any of your vertuous credite. But all is well that is well taken, little sayde is soone amended, and so I pray you pardon your penitent, and sorrowfull offender.

Syr *Strabino* (quoth she) for this fault, you haue already obtayned pardon, it was not so

greeuously taken as you thought for: nor it was
not so fault woorthy as nowe you graunt it. I am
not to exact the vttermost of any man: nor I am
not to conceyue an anger before iust cause be
offred, for you know, that what talke so euer we
vse, that dooth not stretch beyond the boundes of
honest and allowable reason: by promise is to be
esteemed of no effect, therfore I discharge that
Obligation of his full strength and vertue, and
sticke to the promise passed. Mary, yet am I on the
other side, to thinke well of you, that stoode in
such awe of displeasing her: who was far more
afrayd of incurring your anger. Wee women are
not to be too captious nor to quarrellous, neither
to hasty, nor to slowe, for it were no poynt of
ciuillitie to handle our freendes churlishly, and it
were meere folly to quip them vpon no greater
occasion. Fyrst, we are to vnderstand the efficient
cause that vrgeth them to speake, and to way it
thorowly in the wayghts of modestie: and so to
giue aunswere, that we be neyther found to scripi-
lous in the one, nor to coy in the other. I knowe
you are my freend, and so I esteeme you, and as
my freend I make accoumpt of you, then neuer
thinke that I your freend will seeme to conster
your meaning at the wurst: nor yet to condempne
you vpon no greater occasion. I can not deny but
that some are verie apt to anger, to receyue a
matter yll, be it neuer so well spoken, that dooth
demonstrate a great error in her that vseth it,
whatsoeuer: and condempneth her of impudencie,
for her so light beleefe. Soft fyre (they say) maketh sweete mault, a wyse Woman will way all
with discretion: but a foole will be hasty, and to
troublesome to deale with all. Wise *Cato* sayth,

Bridle thine anger with modestie, and iudge not of a matter too rashly, for as there is great commendation in the one: so is there great shame followeth the other. It is a seemely thing for euerie one to vse theyr anger with discretion: because (perchaunce) it may redound to theyr discredite. Thus *Strabino* suffice your selfe, that the coales of my anger were soone kindled and soone quenched. For if I should be angrie with you: you might accoumpt it but the rashnesse of a Woman, and her want of foresight, and so I pray you take it.

    Strabino, perceyuing the courteous excuse of *Cornelia*, and that his passed talke was taken in such gentle gree: thought it now good time to preferre his sute, and so desiring her patience, proceeded as followeth.

¶ Strabino *now offereth his looue*
and seruice to his Lady, requiring the courteous accep-
tion thereof.

Cap. 3.

THEN deere Lady, since neyther my rude behauiour hath offended you, nor my passed presumption purchased any yll will: I hope I may vnder authoritie of your lycence, proceede to the verie ground and effect of all which I haue to vnfolde. For since your wisdome hath weyghed eche cause so discreetly, and construed the meaning thereof with such good demeanour: I will make you partner of my passed perylles, and of the distresse that may ensue, alwayes prouided, that you accept and conceyue no wurse then I thinke it. Since it hath beene my hap (deere Lady) heere in *Verona*, to passe my time in studious exercise, according to the long desired wishe of my Parentes: I haue one way profited, and an other way procured my peryll, for casting mine eyes among the renowned troupe of gallant Dames, (as heere are many) the bountifull beautie of one among all the rest, hath so searched the secretes of my hydden heart, and bewitched my wittes in such woonderfull wise: that neyther medicines may serue to mittigate, hearbes, or any Phisicall potion adiuuate to amendment: but only that soueraigne salue which most dooth delight me, her little finger would lyft me to life, a woord of her mouth would cease all my sorrowes, and one question absolued: would make me a sufficient Scholler. I presume in place, where I behold this seemely shee: and the more I come in her company: the greater increaseth my care, the more I looke: the more I lyke, but lyking brings such restlesse woe: that were it not I had a soule to saue, and that I stand in awe of the anger of God: I should finish this Tragedie, with such a mercilesse massacring of my poore selfe, that neyther should she vaunt of the losse of my life: nor I be thought to demerit so dyrefull a death. But what needeth all these woordes? to what ende doo I make this tedious protestation? my helpe is neuer the more furdred, but by talking of her I am the more endamaged.

Ah Sir (quoth *Cornelia*) is the winde in that doore now? are you Sea sick so soone, and not halfe a myle ouer? well, well, this litle sparke will flame to so fierce a fire: that perhaps all the wit

you haue is not able to quench it. Why Lady
(quoth he) I am not so farre ouer shooes: but I
may returne yet drie, nor I am not so far in, but I
may easily escape out, there is more wayes to the
wood then one, and passages wherin are no
peryll. I shall vse my selfe in extremity as I see
occasion: and doubt you not my wyt shall stand
for a warrant. Syr (quoth she) the crafty Foxe
would eate no grapes, no though they fel in his
mouth, the Catte will eate no sweete milke, for
feare of marring her teeth: so you would not
be in looue, no though you might, and when you
are in, you will looue as you lyst.

Oh Syr, soft fyre makes sweete Mault, it is yll
to halt before a Criple, and it were shame to belye
the Diuell. Your owne woordes dooth condempne
you in that you haue spoken: or else you are very
impudent, that you speake you know not what.
Medicines you say, can make no amendment, the
force of Phisicke to helpe you dooth fayle, and
yet you say, there is one soueraigne salue can minister a remedie. O crafty head, your teethe will
not let your tongue lye, in faith it is almost tyme
to byd you good night. Yet to see how you will
maintayne your matter with wresting of woordes,
you would make me beleeue the Moone is made
of greene cheese: In faith Syr no, you must rise
somewhat more early, if you goe beyond me: and
you must deale more subtilly, if you seeke to deceyue me. But truly if you were as mighty a man
of your deede, as you are of your woorde: *Verona* would be little enough to holde you, and
neuer a Woman of them all durst abyde your
stearne countenaunce. You doo well, you will
holde with the Hare, and run with the Hound, and

you would play *Ambodexter,* if you could tell how, but in fayth Syr I haue you at my fingers ende, euen as perfect without booke as you are within.

Strabino with this passed tale was so nipt in the head, that he had scant any thing to say, and when he saw she was so craftie, that his subtill Sophistry did deceyue him: he would with all his heart haue beene farre enough from her presence: or that his talke were to begin againe. For albeit he was a man stoute of his person: yet they that had seene him now, would haue thought he had neither life nor soule left in him. Which when *Cornelia* beheld how sadly he sate, and would speake neuer a woord, how his couller went and came, as though he had lyne a dying: thought it no courtesie to let him languishe so: but to giue him a fresh encouragement to reuiue vp his spyrites. Why Syr *Strabino* (quoth she) is your heart in your hose? Is your corragious countenaunce so soone chaunged to pale and wanny cheekes? Your face makes apparaunce of your greeuous disease, and your lookes bewray you, that you are in looue. But what of that? neuer dismay your selfe with any doubting dread, nor let not my talke so seeme to trouble you, if I haue made a faulte: I aske you forgiuenesse, and if I haue displeased you: I will doo so no more. You know, promise was made, that all should be well accepted, that pertayned to no harme, and that which should passe betweene vs: should not be offensiue to eyther. I for my part am not offended with any thing spoken: and if you are, truly you be to blame. I will leaue your company, if you be not more merie, and will forsake heereafter any more to frequent it. Shake handes and be freendes againe, and tell me who she is that you so faithfully looue: I will stand your freende perhappes in the matter, and if of my selfe I am not able to doo it: I will informe those of it, who (doubt you not) shall bring it to effect.

With that *Strabino* reuiued him selfe out of his browne study, and began smugly to holde vp the head, right wylling he left his so sodayne quandarie: and began to looke vp with a sensorical countenance. His heart that before lay in a hole: was now ready for ioy to leap out at his mouth, his minde that earst was pinched with passions: was now so iocond, that it daunced with ioy, and his couller that before was as pale as ashes: began now as fresh as the redolent Rose, euerie member which before seemed maimed: he could now stretch out to the ninth degree. And if his present seruice might haue wonne him a Wife: he was able to discharge it, and that to the vttermost, besides, his conceytes began to come so nimbly together: that he now rolled in his Rhethoricke, lyke a Flea in a blanquet. Ah courteous *Cornelia* (quoth *Strabino*) how much am I bound in dutie to your seemly self? How much am I indebted to your prudent personage? that with such sweete perswasions, such maydenly and modest motions, such heroycall and singuler actions: hath losed to lybertie a discouraged prisoner, and hath reuiued him to lyfe, who was almost past all hope of recouerie.

Excellent was the opinion of *Valerius Maximus*, who commended the freendly deedes, doone in aduersitie, as for prosperitie will succour it selfe. My selfe may be witnesse, in aduauncing your

freendlines, whose aduersity was vncurable: had I
not obtained councell of so prudent a Phisition.
I thank you for your freendly offer, wishing I
were able to counteruayle it as I would, and that
my might were correspondent to my well meaning intent: then should you see the depth of my
desyre, and haue occasion to thinke you should
not passe vnrewarded. The Lady whome I looue
will be won to your will, the Saint whome I serue:
will fulfill your request, and the least woord of
your mouth, will binde vp the bargaine. So that
doo you but speake: I speede, doo you say yea,
and I shall haue no nay, so much dare I crake of
her credite, and boast of her bountie: that you can
not so soone say the woord: but she will wyllingly
doo the deede.

Cornelia smiling at this gallant glose, and hauing half a coniecture at what marke he aymed to
shoote at: framed such an aunswere as she thought
best her selfe, and to make *Strabinos* sute neuer the
neere. The foolish Flye (quoth she) so long
iesteth with the Candle, that at last she sindgeth
her selfe, the silly Mouse wandreth oft so farre
abroade: that she is taken tardy before she come
home, and the Nightinggale singeth so sweetly,
tyll she fall in a sleepe, and so oftentymes is caught
at vnawares. Lykewise, I haue helde you heere so
long with a pleasaunt tale, that you make me halfe
mistrust my selfe. If your Lady be so wilfull, to
be wonne to my will, and so courteous that she
will come at my call, yea, if I say the woord,
you aske no better bargaine: either I must coniecture, that her affection is greater to me then to
you: or that shee would clayme assurance of me
for your good behauiour. Now credite me *Stra-*

bino, you are wylie in your woordes: yet not so craftie, but I conceyue your meaning.

Qui simulat verbis, nec corde est fidus Amicus:
Tu quoque fac simile: sic Ars deluditur arte.

But yet *Strabino*, let these matters passe, and to come to the poynt, whervpon we haue stoode so long, name me your Lady, what she is, and where she dwelleth: then shall you heare farder what I will doo for you. If so be (quoth *Strabino*) you will promise me no good will shall want on your part, to the fulfylling my request, and that you will not hinder the matter I haue in hand: I will shew you the sweete she, whose captiue I am, and to whose looue I am thus intierly intangled. Syr (quoth she) *Qui ante non cauit, post dolebit*, A man may looue his house well, though he ride not on the roofe, and a man may make a good Mart, yet be no great gayner. There goeth more woordes to a bargayne then one, and other prayers to be vsed beside the *Pater noster*, when you haue tolde me your tale: you shall see what I will say, and though I make you no promise: doubt not but I will please you.

Then tooke *Strabino* vp her glasse that hung at her Gyrdle, and therein he framed many an Amorous countenaunce. At last (quoth *Cornelia*) what fancies finde you there, that makes you so pleasaunt? or haue you a delyght in beholding your owne face? Nay (quoth he) not for the fancie I finde in mine owne face: but for the comely countenaunce that consisteth in my Lady and Mistresse. And haue you found her face there (quoth she). I pray you let me see her, to iudge if I know her. After *Cornelia* had looked a whyle,

she sayd. Why *Strabino,* you promised I should
see that seemely shee, to whom you owe such delightfull looue and loyaltie. And what I promised
(quoth he) hath beene heere performed. As how
(quoth she). Whose face (quoth he) did you behold when I shewed you? Why yours and mine
owne (quoth she). I thought it would come to
such a passe, well I will speake to her, and if she
chaunce to giue her consent: doubt you not but
you shall heare of it. But one thing I can tell ye,
and that you shall perfectly prooue, how shee is
wedded to her will, and maried to her owne
minde: that she had rather lyue a mayden styll,
then be bydden to so bad a breakfast.

That were against reason (quoth he) that she
should be so maryed to her minde: as not to respect one so good as her selfe, or that in disdayning so good a breakfast, be forced to come to a
courser dinner. A little pyttance in the morning:
is better then to be fasting all day, and perhaps, a
good strong stake strooke in the hedge in Summer:
will stand for a good defence in the Winter.

Albeit Syr (quoth she) you are her better: yet
she thinkes it not against reason to lyke before
she looue, and though it be not expedient to giue
the chyldrens bread to dogges: yet will they
lycke the crums that falles from theyr maisters
table. And besides she thinkes, that if she keepe
her stomacke for a good supper: she shall not take
surfeit of her fasting all day. Lykewise, though
the strong stake doo well fortifie the hedge for
Winter: yet if the stake be without other defence:
the Beasts will easily get ouer and spoyle the pas-
ture, and so in tyme vtterly vndooe the owner.

Strabino hauing well and sufficiently pondred

her talke: thought now he would not discourage him selfe with the diuersitie of her deuises, but euen as his heart serued him he would make her an aunswer. Why Lady (quoth he) doo you misdoubt of my bountifull behauiour? or that I am such a one as regardeth not my honesty? Thinke you if I would make my choyse, I could not haue as good as you, or if my minde had beene so adicted, ere this I could not haue beene sped? thinke you all Women are of your minde? or that they will dislyke vpon no occasion? No credit me, *Cornelia* (I speake *Bona fide*) if my stomacke had serued: I could haue beene soone suffised, and if all Women were of your minde: I should haue but a colde sute with my wooing. But belyke you are betrothed already: and that makes you so dayntie, if you be tell me, that I may loose no more labour.

Truly Syr *Strabino* (quoth she) if as yet I am betrothed: it is more then I know, what my Parents haue done, I know not, but as yet I can assure you, there is no such matter meant by me. But what of that, you are neuer the neerer your purpose, nor yet the likelyer to gayne my good wyll, you are a gallant Gentleman, well known in *Verona*, wherfore you may chaunce to lyght on a better bootie, and doubt you not but there are those, who with all theyr hearts would haue you. Wherfore good Syr, neuer feede your humors on such a homely peece: since there be more delycate Damoselles that will not deny you. But now it drawes toward supper tyme, and occasion is so offred: that perforce I must leaue you, desiring you not to deeme any discourtesie, that I leaue your company so soone.

Nay (quoth *Strabino*) I am not to conceyue

the wurst of your departure: but rather to thanke
you, that vouchsaued my company so long, no
anger I trust is conceyued for my superfluous
speeche: but rather pardoned for that no dishon-
estie was meant. Thus thanking you a thousand
tymes for your courtesie offered: tyll Fortune so
frame our next meeting together, I commend you
to God, whome I pray graunt me my wishe, and
you the depth of your desire.

Thus Gentlemen is *Cornelia* and *Strabino*
parted, he taking the way home to his Chamber:
and she speedeth her selfe that she were at supper,
but so sowre a sauce she had giuen *Strabino:* that
the sharpnesse turned his stomacke from minding
any meate. It is not straunge to see what a metamorphesis Looue maketh of a man? that he which
earst might haue bragged with the best: is now become to carefull for any company, he which earst
walked the streetes with a gallant grace: nowe
pulleth his bonet ouer his browes, that none may
beholde his sodayne alteration? He which before
lyued merily, faring with the finest, and delyght-
ing in the dayntiest: now scant eateth a good
meales meate in a month. He commeth to his
Chamber, throweth him selfe on his bed, incombred with so many cares, that it is vnspeakable: at
last vnto him selfe talketh in this order.

O God, where are become the loftie lookes I
vsed before I was a Loouer? Where are the curious
countenaunces, the wayghtie woordes, the dayntie dealinges, the bolde behauiours, and the manly
order of lyfe wherein I lyued before? Hath Looue
so puissaunt a power to reuert my sweetnesse into
sorrowes, my myrth into mazednesse, my life into
langor, and all my happinesse into a state so help-

lesse? O greefe without ende, O sorrowes without
ceasing, O hellish tormentes that hath no conclusion. But yet am I the first that was framed to
folly? Or I am the last that shall be lead by Looue?
Hath not the Gods themselues beene subiect to
lyke mestiue miseries? Did not *Iupiter* enter *Acri-
sius* tower, in the shape of a fayre swimming
Swan, to deflowre faire *Danea? Apollo* persecuted
Daphne to get his will of her: *Neptune* begatte
Nauplius father to *Palamedes* of *Amimone*,
daughter of *Danæus: Mercurie* lay with *Lar* the
beautifull *Nimphe*, and got of her two prety chyldren called *Lares*. Likewise king *Dauid* became
coninced by the looue of *Bersaba: Salomon* the
wise was subiect to looue likewise. If then looue
hath made the Gods to agree, the wise to be wilfull, the stoutest to stoupe: is it possyble for me
poore *Strabino*, to resist a thing of such force? O
Cornelia, lyttle doost thou esteeme the good wyll
I beare thee, lyttle doost thou accoumpt of my
constancie, lyttle doost thou regard my restlesse
rage, and little doost thou deeme all my dollorous
doubtes. Is thy heart so frosen, that the sunny
beames of bounty may not make it to melt? Is thy
minde so misbeleeuing, that no faithfull fidelitie
may seeme to reforme it? Is not dayly proofe
sufficient to trye my trustinesse? Is not the great
good will I beare thee, able to cause thee to accoumpt well of me? To offer me crueltie for courtesie, thou doost me open iniurie. Alas wretched
wight that I am, whose miserie is more then mine?
Whose dayes more dollorous, whose tyme more
troublesome, whose life more loathsome, and
whose state more yrksome, the day to me is nothing delightfull: the night more carefull, sleepe I

can not, and waking, I neuer cease wayling.

Sometime I syt to conquere the cogitations, which weary my wittes: then againe am I driuen into a more deepe desire. Sometime I scorne and laugh at Looue, thinking mine owne wyll a sufficient warrant: but then in a moment aryseth manifolde miseries, so that neither waking nor sleeping, walking or sitting, can my sorrowfull selfe sustayne any rest. Why wast thou borne to abide such bitternesse? why hast thou lyued to see this trystfull tyme? why hath not death desired his due: and the graue cutte of this mercilesse greefe? O Laberinth of intricate euylles, O maze of endlesse myseries, whome neither dutifull surrendring of my selfe may suffise: nor any vertuous action seeme to content you. Cease *Strabino*, giue not thy selfe altogether to insolencie, nor frame not thy selfe wholy vanquished with follyes, time may turne thy troubles to tranquilitie, tyme may make thy foes thy freendes, and tyme may reuert all thy paynes to pleasure. Impute not thy Lady altogether disloyall, for he that speedeth at the first: wooeth well, and he that hath no denyall: in my opinion is very fortunate.

In these and such lyke carefull complayntes the solytarie *Strabino* hath worne away the wearysome night. In the morning commeth his brother and freend *Rodolfo*, to vnderstand the cause of his sodaine sicknesse.

¶ Rodolfo, *the brother of* Cornelia, *and auouched freend to* Strabino, *commeth to the Chamber to knowe the cause of his sicknesse.*

Cap. 4.

AT LAST *Rodolfo* a deere freende to *Strabino*, and Brother to his Lady and Mistresse, myssing his freend from Schoole, wherto was his dayly repayre: commeth to his Chamber, and there found him tossing and turmoyling him selfe, on his carefull coutch, which when he sawe, as one amased at this sodayne mutabilitie, and greatly greeued to see his freend in such a pittious plyght: beganne thus to frame his speeche.

My deerest freend and cheefest Iewell of my ioy, not so glad of the rare freendship that in you I haue found: as sorrowfull to see this vncouth sight. Is this the comely countenaunce that you were wont to carie: and now chaunged into the perfect Image of care? Are you that man, that earst dyd swim in delyght: and now bereft of your former behauiour? Was my woordes earst woorthy to procure thee to pleasure: and now not able to stand in their former effect? Am not I the same *Rodolfo* I was wont to be: and shall not I nowe be accoumpted as thy former freend?

What is the cause my *Strabino* of this sodayne alteration? How happens it you are so soone chaunged into heauines? If I be woorthy to know the cause of your carefulnesse, or that my desertes may gayne my desire: let me vnderstand the sum of your sorrowes, and doubt not but I will see some redresse for you.

Strabino hauing well wayed the woordes of his freend, and how earnest he was in this his request: bethought him selfe how he might sufficiently aunswer him, and yet not be found tardy in his talke. Perhappes afterward he would discouer more of the case: but at this instaunt he should not knowe whome he looued, wherefore in this order he framed his aunswere. My deere *Rodolfo*, whose freendshippe I highly make accoumpt of, and whose fidelitie I haue found firme in waighty affayres, to you will I display my dollorous dis-ease: hoping by your meanes it may be mittigated.

Since first it was my fortune (deere freend) to vse the company of the braue Ladyes and Damo-sels heere in *Verona:* I haue been attainted with so many perillous passions: that sure I am past hope to haue any recouerie, yet doo I striue with mine affection as forceably as I can: but vnpossible it is for me to remooue it, so excellently doo I esteeme of the person, whome I honour: that in lyfe or death I am hers at commaund.

Rodolfo perceyuing *Strabinos* sicknesse, and how that looue made him to languish in such sort: he esteemed the matter of lesse accoumpt, and made him an aunswer but little to please him. Ah Syr (quoth he) are coales so soone kindled in your vncertaine stomack? is your minde so mu-table, that no stedfast stay may be had? Are you one that regardeth not your prosperitie: or make you so small accoumpt to fall into miserie? Doo you see the daunger each day before your eyes: and are so heedelesse to fall headlong in the same? You haue read your selfe, how the effectes of Looue are straunge: and by so much as you haue seene and heard, me thinkes it should be odious

vnto you. Forget you *Plautus* woords, when as
touching this diuellish disease, he sayth: *Iactor,*
crucior, agitor, stimulor, versor in amoris rota,
miser exanimor, feror, distrahor diripior, vbi non
sum: ibi sum, ibi est animus. How like you this
lesson alleadged to your Looue? How can you
excuse that these feares are not felt? How can you
disprooue these innumerable daungers? Remember *Antigonus* woordes to his Father *Demetrius.*
Let *Seleucus* folly to his sonne, forwarne thee
what aduersenesse consisteth in this contagious
disease, who ioyned his owne Wife with his sonne
in mariage to satisfie his lust. What caused the
long dissencion between *Themistocles* and *Aris-*
tides: but the looue of *Stesilia* the harlot? What
procured the hatred betweene *Cato* and *Cæsar:* but
the lycentious looue after *Seruilia* the strumpette?
Semiramis, honored and extolled for her noble-
nesse of minde, and vertue in her deedes: by looue
brought her name into eternall infamie. Why are
the *Assirian* Kinges so prorooued of wantonnes:
but for the lawlesse looue they vse, with theyr
Concubines? Dyd not looue blemishe the rare renowne of *Hanniball* in *Salapia?* Dyd not looue
infect the fame of *Alexander?* What caused *Cata-*
lin to kyll his sonne *Oristilla:* but looue? What
caused *Laodice* Wife to *Ariartes* King of *Cappa-*
docia to murder his sonnes: but looue? What made
Scilla to destroy her Father: but looue? What
made the stately walles of *Troy* be sacked: but
looue? Infinite are the extremities which through
looue aryse, and can not be so much reprehended:
as by right it deserueth. What man so wilfull to
come subiect to Women? What paynes more in-
tollerable then to come at theyr calles? It is theyr

ioye, to haue one bowe at theyr beckes, it is theyr
delight to haue one wayte on theyr wylles, it is
the cheefest of theyr choyse, to haue a man sue for
theyr succour. Then Gyll will be a Gentlewoman,
if she could but *Parle vn petit de Francoys*. If a
man will be made a meacock, and blinde him selfe
with a little of theyr bolde behauior: then is theyr
coyne currant, yea, better syluer then an honester
Womans. If they can once fledge them selues, with
an other mannes fethers, and iet in theyr Iewelles
at other mens costes: then a pin for the prowdest,
a fygge for the finest, she is as honest as the best,
though she be ashamed to vse it, yet sure she dooth
well, not to haue her honestie so much seene, least
with wearing it on working dayes, it may catch
to much heat, and so melt it away: or els take so
much colde, that it wil neuer be good after. If with
a song, you would be sung a sleepe, or with a
daunce lead to delight, or if you haue the *Quatri-
nos*, to play at sinke and syse: then is she a Companion with the cunningest, a fellowe with the
forwardest, and will rather play small game: then
syt quite out. Who would misse such a mate, that
for a monthes pleasure: will after make you leade
a loathsome life? Who would lacke such a Lasse,
that for a dayes pride: will make you goe a moneth
starke naked? Now truly he were vnwise, that
would not haue such a Wenche, and he were too
farre foolishe, that would want such a *Bon Companion*.

Oh *Strabino*, in fayth the blacke Oxe neuer
trode on your foote yet, you neuer came where it
grewe: nor you neuer tryed time, as heere after
you shall finde it. If you had beaten the bush, and
caught any of the Byrds: I doubt not but you

would haue tolde me an other tale. If you be wise: stay your selfe in this state, if you will followe your freends who wishe you well: eate a bushell of Salt with them, ere you trust any one of them, for you were better beware before: then wishe you had taken heede, when it is too late. Trye and then trust mee, if you finde not true that I haue tolde you: then report of mee, as my deedes shall giue occasion.

Strabino hauing lyne still a pretie whyle, and deuised howe he might now stand in defence of his Misterisse: made aunswere vnto his freend on this wise. Syr (quoth he) saying and dooing are two mens labours, and it is easier for a man to promise: then to fulfill, your selfe now setteth such a corragious countenaunce on the matter: as though your minde were inuincible. Thinke you there is not as wise men in the world as you? Are you made of such mettall, as force will not melt you? could you if the matter were brought to the tryall: with all the cunning you haue make any resistaunce? No credit me, but euen so glad to finde ease as my self: and march vnder *Cupids* banner for company. What sayd *Ariosto* in the commendation of Looue? He sayth, what sweeter state? what more bountifull blysse, and what more happy life: then to be lyncked in looue? *Chrisippus* also sayth, that looue is the bond of freendship, and ought not to be helde in contempt: for that beauty is the flowre of vertue. *Cicero* holdeth opinion, that a Wise man may lawfully looue, and the very reciprocall and mutuall societie of true and faithfull freendship (say the *Peripatetions*) is Looue. *Zeno* the Prince of the *Stoikes* affirmeth, that it is needefull and necessarie of

young men to be loouers, and neuer disagreeeth
with wise men: for that Looue is an associate with
vertue. And will you reprooue Looue that is so
much honored? Will you disdayne Looue that is
so magnified? Will you condemne all Women, although some be euill? and will you reprehend
all Women for one strumpets sake? What perillous
paines? What troublesome trauaile? What pinching panges, and what manifolde miseries, dyd one
woman sustaine for you? Remember her that
brought you into this world, consider her care in
prouiding for your prosperity, thinke on the
dayly deuises her motherly affection framed to
keepe you in quiet, sometime lulling on the lap,
and trifling with many a toy, for the pure looue
she bare her childe, remember all these poynts
indifferently: and then iudge how much you are
bound vnto that famous sex. Did not God giue
Adam in Paradise a Woman for his companion?
Hath not God ordained man and woman to liue
together in matrimony? and that the mutuall looue
betweene man and wife, is to him most acceptable? O my freend *Rodolfo*, forsake this fondnes,
leaue of this lewdnes, and take holde on a better
text, looue them that looue you, and maintayne
no more this vaine assertion. When *Rodolfo* had
wayed the sick mans aunswer, and that he was so
farre in: that it was too late to crye hoe, he sayd.
Now credit me *Strabino*, all women haue iust
cause to wage you well: because you stand in
their defence so doubtily, were I a woman: you
should not want what possibility could performe,
and sure I would chuse you alwayes for my
Champion against any whatsoeuer. And truly,
she whome you looue, knowing what mettall you

are made of: if she looue you not againe, she is very vncurteous.

Well, I warrant you, ye will not dye of this disease, you will take better aduisement with you I hope. If you would frequent the Tournaments, to bestride the stately Steedes, and with the shiuering Launce to behaue your selfe manfully: these foolishe fancies, these troublesome thoughtes, and these coy cogitations would soone abandon you. The howre you know of our exercise is at hand, I must be gon, my Companions attend my comming, in the after noone I will visit you againe. Your sodayne departure (quoth *Strabino*) is an augmenting of my greefe, but I will not hinder you from your valiaunt exercise: tyll you come agayne, God keepe you.

Rodolfo beeing departed: *Strabino* could not take any rest, vp he rose, his head incombred with a thousand thoughts, his minde musing on many matters. One whyle he thought to goe see his sweete Saint: then he thought it would but procure the greater payne, an other whyle he thought to send to her: then he doubted how she would take the matter, at last, he tooke pen, inke and paper, and framed his salutations, as followeth.

Albeit deere Mistresse, you may accoumpt me more wytlesse, then wise, and more saucie then beseemeth me, to perturbe your patience, with these friuolous lynes: yet if you respect the good will I wishe you, and consider the dutifull seruice I am ready to showe you: I trust I shall be discharged of any crime committed, and that my honest intent deserueth no rashe repulse. Part of my paines I haue bewrayed to your bounty, and some of my sorrowes you haue secretly seene: then iudge if my iustnes deserues not your gentlenes, and whether my constancie may claime part of your courtesie. *Pigmalion* so long imbraced a colde stone: that at last he wonne the same to his Wife. *Admetus* in the attyre of a man, with long seruice gayned his best beloued. If Looue were so effectuall to frame, fit for theyr fancies: why may not *Strabinos* hap at length returne fortunate? But perhappes deere Mistresse, you will alleadge that the lybertie of my speech, bewrayeth the lyghtnesse of my Looue, and that I seeme to vndermine you with forgerie, intending no fidelytie. To driue you out of such doubts, and discharge my selfe of double dealing, and to prooue my looue vehement without vaunting, feruent without falsehood, trusty without trifling, and constant without any craftinesse: let be practised for proofe, what shall please you to imploy me: and commaund to the vttermost, though it were losse of my lyfe. If you finde me faltring: then rightly repell me, and if you prooue me periured: then neuer more vse me. Thus committing the sum of my sute to your sweete solution, and the construing of my cause to your inestimable courtesie: I referre heere to multiply manifolde matters, and so with a Courteous *Conge*, byd you farewell hartily.

Yours to commaund, the solitary *Strabino*.

This Letter thus written, and sealed with sorrowes: he wished a thousand times it were in the hands of his courteous *Cornelia*. But now thought he, how might I behaue my selfe in the sending my sute? Howe might I deuise to haue

this delyuered? If I carie it my selfe: I shall be
suspected, if I send it by a straunger: her Father
may chaunce to see it. If I should make my freend
Rodolfo messenger, hee would then perceyue the
sum of my secretes, then would hee see that his
Sister were my Saint, and that her looue would
set me at lybertie. I knowe not how the matter
may be misvsed: nor how the cause may be by
them consulted. A bargayne (they say) well made
is halfe won, and he that woorkes surely: lightly
hath no harme, then will I trust none in this but
my selfe: so if I speede not well, none knowes it
but my selfe.

The Tournaments beeing ended: *Rodolfo* returned, and finding *Strabino* walking in his Chamber: requested to know how he felt him selfe
amended? Quoth *Strabino*, neyther amended, nor
wurse impayred: but euen as you left me, yet if
it were not for hope: the heart could not holde,
so I hope that my sicknesse, will in the ende returne my sweetnesse. Walking I thinke will somewhat mittigate the mazednesse of my minde, and
beside make me haue a stomacke the better to my
meate: if it shall please you to walke with me: I
wyll after goe with you to your Fathers house.
With right good wyll (quoth *Rodolfo*) I wyll
walke where you please, and doo what you can
deuise: so that I might somewhat perswade you
from looue.

¶ Signor Truculento, *an extorting*

Vsurer in Verona, *commeth to the house of* Giorolamo Ruscelli, *the father of* Cornelia, *to desire
his Daughter in mariage, and bring-
eth with him a sumptuous
present.*

Cap. 5.

LEAVING *Rodolfo* and *Strabino* in walking for
theyr pleasure: I wyll now rehearse how olde
Signor Truculento smoutched vp him selfe in his
Fustian slyppers, and put on his holy day hose, to
come a wooing to Mistresse *Cornelia.* The olde
horson would needes be lusty, and to cheerishe vp
his churlishe carkase, would get him a wanton
Wife. And though I say it, he was as well made a
man, and as curious in his quallities: as euer an
olde Horse in this towne, when he is gnabling on
a thystle. This carpet Knight, hauing pounced him
selfe vp in his perfumes, and walking so nice on the
ground, that he would scant bruse an Onion:
comes to the house of *Signor Giorolamo Ruscelli,*
bringing with him a verie costly Cuppe, wherein
was about fiue hundred Crownes. When he was
come into the presence of the Gentleman, he sayd.
Syr, as one right glad to heare of your health, and
willing besides to woorke your well fare: I am
come to see how it fareth with you, because that
long tyme I haue beene desirous. First Syr, this
Cuppe I freely giue you, and these fiue hundred
Crownes, I frankly bestowe on you, besides if you
pleasure me in my reasonable request: you shall

finde me your freend in more then I wyll
speake of.

The Gentleman amazed at *Truculentos* lyber-
alytie, who before would scant bestowe on him
selfe a good meales meate for expence of money:
made him this aunswere. I can not chuse Syr, but
consider well of your courtesie, and lykewise esteeme of your bountifull beneuolence, vndeserued
of my part to be so rytchly rewarded: considering my countenaunce to you hath beene small.
And if your request be so reasonable as you seeme
to affyrme, and that it lyeth in me to bring the
same to effect: doubt not that I will make you
any denyall, since you haue gratified me with so
great a gyft. Well Syr, now *Truculento* trusseth
vp his towardnesse, and bustleth vp his braynes
lyke a bunch of Radishe, setting vp his wyttes to
woorke about his Amorous eloquence: he thus began to tell foorth his tale. It may be thought to you
good Syr, eyther a naturall inclination, or a pre-
destinate desire, that a man of my yeeres should
now be bent to folly, in crauing that company
which a youthfull head requyreth, and seeking to
match my selfe in mariage, drawing each day to
my death. But as a good foresight in all thinges is
to be had, and dillygent industry keepes the
Woolfe from the doore. Euen so, though I am to
be thought fonde in following my wyll, I am to
be excused in wishing my weale. Yet this may be
alleadged to condemne mine assertion, and this may
be thought, I do it more for lust then looue. That
in making my choyse, I am not more cyrcumspect, and in ruling my will, I am not more wise.
The hoary heayres should chuse one agreeable to
his age, the lusty youth one meete to his tender

tyme: then if this allegation may stand in effect, I haue made my market farre amisse. On age I begin to bend my browes: and on a gallant Girle I fire my fancie, Age of me is altogether despised: and youthfull yeeres honored and exalted, Age in my minde is nothing holsome: but beauty is braue, delycate and toothsome. So Syr, if I may gaine her whom I haue thus chosen: I shall not be only pleasured, but your selfe for euer heereafter profited. Your Daughter it is whome I desire, it is euen she whom I serue, and none but she must be my solace. If you accept my sute, make aunswer accordingly: and if I shall haue your Daughter, doo not deny me.

The Gentleman hauing well lystened this newe come wooers tale, and seeing at what marke he leueld his looue, he beeing one him selfe that preferred money before manly modestie, coyne before courteous ciuillitie, and rytches before any vertuous action, besides, ouercome with the costlynesse of the Cuppe, out of measure contented with the fiue hundred Crownes: Furthermore he thought, if he matched his daughter with him: she would soone send him to Church, and then should she swym in her golden bagges: was verie lothe to send away such a sweete Suter, thinking it rare to haue a rytcher: wherefore to *Truculento* he made this aunswere.

I hope Syr, you doubt not of the good will I wishe you, nor of the courtesie you shall finde heereafter, your reasonable request is altogether allowed: and your gentle gyft greatly accepted. I would my Daughters dowrie were as much as I could wishe it: I would bestowe it on no man sooner then your selfe. With that he called for his

Daughter *Cornelia*, who when she was come into this olde amorous Squyres presence: his heart began to heaue lyke a Bakers bun, his whole complexion so myraculously chaunged: that you could scant haue knowen him from a Croydon sanguine. Oh so his Amorous eyes beganne to looke on his new Wife, I am sure he would haue spent all the shooes in his shop to haue had one kysse for a courteous *Conge*.

Loe Daughter (quoth her Father) God hath sent you heere a Husbande, one that will maintayne you in your brauerie with the best, and you shall lacke nothing, but lyue a Ladyes lyfe, now make aunswere as you shall thinke best.

Cornelia somewhat mooued at this made matter, and nothing contented with her Fathers choyse, all her senses distracted with this sodayne motion: yet tooke corrage to aunswere the matter in this sort. Deere Father, it is the duty of the Chylde to be obedient to her Parentes preceptes: and it is the Fathers fame to haue his Chylde vertuously nurtured, I confesse it is my part to obay your graue aduise: and it ought to be your care to see me meetely matched. If then your care be no better bestowed: my dutie must be as much neglected, though your will be to see me carelesly cast away, if it lye in me, I am to preuent it, bothe for the credit of your woorthy estate: and also for the good name of my simple selfe. Wyll you for money marrie me to a myser? Wyll you for wealth wedde me to a Wyttoll? And wyll you for rytches so lyttle regard me? Shall I for a lyttle vaine glorie, forsake vertue? Shall I for paltrie pride run headlong to hell? Shall I for mortall muck, forsake immortality? No Father, had he wytte to his wealth: he would be more wise, had he reason to his rytches, he would be of more regard, and had he manhood to his money: he would be ashamed of his extorting vsury. For what is wealth without wisdome? Ritches without reason, and money disorderly gouerned? Euen lyke the shadowe of a man portraited in a picture, that hath all the lyneaments in good order belonging to a man: yet wants the man him selfe, for as the Image lacketh lyfe to his proper proportion: so this man wants that which should most of all adorne him. Rather had I you should haue chosen a countrey Clowne, that getteth his lyuing lawfully, and lyueth by trueth and honesty: then such a one as is not acquainted with any vertuous behauiour. I must confesse he is wise enough, to make much of his money, and carefull beside how to cull in his coyne, but he that will run to the diuell for a lyttle drosse: and pinche the poore to the perdition of his owne soule: shall neuer be looued of me whyle I liue, much lesse intende I to haue him to my Husband.

When *Truculento* heard *Cornelias* pinching reply, and how she disdayned such a loathsome lyuer: he would with all his heart haue had his Cup againe, on condition he would neuer come more a wooing. Yet set he a good face on the matter, because he would not be misdoubted, and fayne he would haue spoken, but his heart was so bigge he could not, the which her Father seeing, sayd.

Come Syr, we will goe walke about the Cittie a whyle, and neuer dismay your selfe at the woordes of my Daughter, for will she, nill she: I will haue her followe my minde in this matter. Away went olde *Truculento* with a heauy heart, yet the Gentlemans woordes, procured him to be of better cheere.

They were no sooner out of the doore: but in came *Rodolfo* and *Strabino* bothe together, and *Strabino* in walking: had bewrayed to his freend the sum of his secretes, whereto he gayned so much his good will: that he promised he would further it as much as he might. When they came into the Garden: there they found *Cornelia* very sad and sorowfull. Why Syster (quoth *Rodolfo*) how happens it that you seeme so sad? Why doo you cumber your minde with carefulnesse, your head with heauinesse, and all your parts with such pensiuenesse? When I went foorth in the morning: you were merrie, and are you now chaunged into such melancholie? O Brother (quoth she) after myrth commeth mones, after ioy greefe, and after pleasure paine, that comes in an howre: that happens not in seuen yeere: Euen so since your departure, hath chaunced such chaunge: that all my freends will lament to heare of my fathers folly. Hath my father (quoth *Rodolfo*) framed things contrary to your fancie? And dooth his dealings hinder your delight? I pray you vnfolde this sodayn alteration: if I may be so bolde to craue such courtesie. You are to commaund me in greater affayres then this quoth she: wherfore attend and I wyll tell you all. Not fully yet two howres agoe, there came to my father such a comely *Camellion:* that could chaunge himselfe into all hues sauing honesty, all quallities in him, sauing those that are comly, and as expert in humanity: as he that neuer knew what it meant. Besides (but that I am not to reprehend age, for that it is honorable, nor to condemne his yeeres, for that he hath liued a tranquile tyme) he is as doting a dissard as any in *Verona,* and as couetous a Carle, as lyueth at this day. But if wealth may make a man wise: he will brag with the best, or his extortion make him esteemed: he wyll be nothing behinde hand. But if vertue should vaunt and clayme for her fee: this comely Squyre were sunk in the wetting, and all his credite crackt before it were gotten. But to come to the effect of the matter, and to let passe his properties: without they were prayse woorthy, and to shew the cause of his comming, and his sute to my Father. It is so, that this money myser: is become a lusty loouer, and bringing a gorgious gift to gratify my Father: the Amorous whorson would haue me to his wife. Now my father (as you know) hath a good minde to money, and lookes that the olde suter will soone turne vp his heeles, (so then shall I haue more money then modest manners, and greater store of substaunce, then wisedome to rule it,) he would needes make him promise, that he should wedde me to his Wife. But I gaue him such a cooling carde, and such a pinching replye: that my Father is fayne to goe and perswade him, saying at his departure: that he shall haue me whether I wyll or no. But sure, ere I giue my consent to fulfill his fancie, and match my selfe with such a *Midas:* my Father shall first cause me leaue my lyfe, which wyll be a greater reward: then to lyue with reproche.

Now surely Syster (quoth *Rodolfo*) I must commend your constancie, and allow the care of your credit, before such a doting drudge should spoyle your gallant youth: my selfe would tell my Father an other tale. With that *Strabino* tooke

out his Letter, and courteously kissing it: gaue it
to his sweete Saint, and in the meane whyle she
was in reading it: they walked about the Garden
together, and hauing read it: came vnto him saying. Syr *Strabino,* your honest intent: I can not
dislyke, nor your well meaning minde can I reprooue, but wishe I were woorthy so seemely a
suter, and of abyllitie to gratifie your exceeding
courtesie. I confesse your iustnesse condempneth
me of vngentlenesse, and your constancie re-
prooueth my great discourtesie, in that at your
last departure: I dyd misuse my selfe with such
blunt behauiour, but as the Sunne should not set
on an anger conceyued: so I hope my presumption by you was pardoned. If at the first I had
graunted your looue: you might haue alleadged my
minde to be lyght, if at the first demaund I had
made no deniall: you might haue thought me very
vntrustie, but now perceyuing your ardent affection, the loyall looue and good wyll you beare me:
I think I can not bestowe my selfe better, then on
him whose fidelytie I haue found so faithfull.

Now Brother tell me how lyke you my
choyse? In choosing my freend, Syster (quoth
Rodolfo) you haue followed my fancie, in making my freend your Husband: you haue doone as
I would haue you. God graunt your dayes may be
spent so prosperous: as I wishe this match to each
party meritorious. This match is more seemely:
then my Fathers forecasting, and this is more
agreeable to God: then to haue you vnited in that
order, for where perfect looue is effectually
placed: there is triumphant tranquillitie, peace and
plentie, Gods blessing and sufficient. But where
mariage is made vpon compulsion, the one agree-

ing, the other disdayning: there is dayly discorde,
displeasing of God, continuall care, and many
infirmities followeth. Wherefore I thinke this a
match so meete: that it can not be mended, a
choyse so equall: as there can be no better, heere
is looue and loyaltie, heere is fayth and fidelitie,
God prospere your proceeding, I wishe it hartily.

Now Gentlemen, iudge if *Strabino* had not
cause to be corragious of so gallant a conquest? of
so peerelesse a prize, and so loouing a Lady?
Whose ioy was more iocond? Whose blisse more
bountifull? And whose hap might be compared to
Strabinos good lucke, in compassing that in a moment: which he thought would neuer haue come
to effect, and in getting the good wyll of so gallant a Goddesse, so sweete a Saint, and so mercifull
a Mistresse.

Wherefore now leauing the languishing of his
sorrowfull sicknesse, and forsaking the feare that
earst followed his fancie: he saluteth his Lady
with this courteous replye. I see (most mercifull
Mistresse) that there is no disease so desperate: but
helpe may be had, no sicknesse so sore: but
Phisicke can foyle it, no wound so daungerous:
but a sweete salue can recure it, no greefe so great:
but patience bringes prosperitie, and no doubt so
dreadfull: but tyme bringeth to full effect. See
heere, he that was earst drowned in doubtes: now
hoysed in happynesse, he that earst remayned in
vnmercifull myserie: nowe floteth in florishing
felycitie, he that earst was plundged in pittyfull
perplexitie: hath chaunged his state to perfect
prosperitie. If *Cæsar* heere would commit to me
all his conquers, *Cræsus* his puissant possessions, or
the three Goddesses proffer vnto me, as they dyd

to *Paris:* None could so much please me, as you
my second selfe, none could more delyght me:
then my Iewell so gentle, nor any more lyke me
then my Lady so loyall, whose courteous constancie: high *Ioue* prosper in perpetuitie.

Cornelia seeing *Strabino* in the myddest of his
myrth, and hauing deuised a drift to fal pat to their
pleasures, crossed his tale with a courteous kysse,
and after began her talke in this order. The wise
holde opinion (quoth she) that a present peryll is
good to be preuented, who woorkes warely at
the first: neede not repent him after, and a bargayne well made, is halfe won. You knowe
Brother, our Father requyreth rytches out of
measure, and a match of money makes vp his
mouth, nowe if *Strabino* should solycite his sute
to him (as needes he must) he may alleadge the
want of his wealth, and that his abillitie is not able
to maintayne me according to his minde, as no
doubt he will compasse a hundred conceyts: because he would match me with olde *Truculento*.

To deceyue him now of this deuise, and to
winne the matter fit for our wyll: I haue bethought of a cunning coniecture, and remembred
such a remedy, as will fall verie fyt, bothe that my
Father shall giue his consent: and the olde worldly
wretch serued in his right kinde. First, Brother
you shall goe with *Strabino* to *Truculentos* house,
and there on your credite, take vp a great summe
of money, as much as you shall thinke good, then
go you into *La strada di San Paolo*, and buy the
Iewell which my Father hath long had such great
affection to, the which will so win him: that I
dare warrant none but you shall haue me to his
Wife. For the payment therof you shall not neede

greatly to accoumpt: for that you shall referre vnto me, but this way I thinke you shall soonest speede, and this way I warrant you shall gayne no nay.

I perceyue Syster (quoth *Rodolfo*) a Womans wyt is good at a neede, and this your deuise full well we allowe. Howe say you *Strabino*, shall we put this in practise? Or wyll you deferre it for feare of discredite? Nay sure (quoth *Strabino*) since the matter consisteth on no greater a clause, and that this inuencion may driue all out of doubt: I thinke eache day a yeere tyll we haue dispatched it, and eache howre a month tyll we haue bound vp the bargayne.

Cornelia espying her Father was entred, and fearing least he would mistrust the matter, gaue them a watche woord to win them away, and to goe about their pretended purpose. *Rodolfo* goes in to flatter his Father, in the meane whyle *Strabino* stealeth out, so that theyr prancks were nothing perceyued: but all fell out, euen as they would wishe it. *Rodolfo* stealeth out, and followeth his freend, and in short tyme they met bothe together, then they agreeed how the case should be concluded: if so be the money would be lent that they hoped for.

They beeing come to *Signor Truculentos* house, and he sitting at his doore verie solytarie: *Rodolfo* in the freendlyest fashion saluteth him, and flattering the foole, thus frameth his tale. Woorthy Syr, if I say otherwayes then beseemes me: I hope you wyll beare with me, and if I speake as affection serues me: I doubt not but you wyll deeme all at the best: so that neyther flattering you with any forgerie, nor vpholding my selfe by any vaine glorie: I shall committe to your courtesie my well meaning tale, and my simple sute to be accoumpted of, as you shall lyke best.

Since the prouidence of the Gods hath so appointed, law of nature hath eke allowed, and the graue aduise of my Father hath so consented, that you are the only man must matche with my Sister: I reioyce that my hap hath prooued so fortunate, and that the Gods hath sent me such a lucky lot, as your woorthy selfe shall become my brother, always wishing that your tyme may prooue as tranquill, as my good wyll is to woorke your well fare. When olde *Truculento* heard *Rodolfos* Rhetoricke, and how gallantly he glosed to purchase his purpose, he thinking that all his tale had beene trueth, and vpon pure affection he had spoken the same, replyed. Freend *Rodolfo:* You haue not found me so bountifull: as heereafter you shall find me brotherlike, ne haue you had any such occasion to commend me: as heereafter you shall purchase occasion to prayse me. I remayne to pleasure you, in what I can possible, and will stand your freend in more then I will speake of. Indeede your Father hath found me so freendly: that I thanke him, he deemes me to deserue his Daughter, and you I see conceyue so good opinion of me: that you thinke me sufficient to match with your Syster. Well, if all prooue so well, as I hope it will, and the matche be so graunted as on my part it is proffered, it is not money, or ought that I haue, but shall be all present to doo you a pleasure.

Strabino began to smyle in his sleeue. *Rodolfo* much a doo to keepe his countenaunce, to see the olde whorson how willing he was: and how

craftily they caught him into so good a beleefe,
wherefore nowe he beginneth to shewe foorth his
sute: not doubting to speede before they departed.
Well Syr (quoth *Rodolfo*) for your proffered
courtesie I remayne your debtor, not doubting
but the matter will come so to passe as I haue alwayes wished it, and if it lyke you so well, as to
graunt me one request: whyle I liue you shall
binde me to the vttermost of my power. Heere
is a Gentleman, a verie deere freend and fellow of
mine, who because his liuing is not yet come into
his handes: is desirous to borrowe a certayne sum
of money, allowing for the gaynes thereof, what
you will demaund: the sum dooth amount to
fowre thousand Duckattes, and but for one
month he desireth the lending, and if by that
tyme he doo not discharge the debt: he is willing
to forfayte his patrimony, and besydes the best
lym of his body.

Freend *Rodolfo* (quoth *Truculento*) the world
is so wretched now a dayes, and diuers of the people so pinched by pouerty: that many will borrow, but slack payment is made, then if we exact
the Law to the vttermost: we are accoumpted
couetous carles, worldly wretches, and such like,
which makes me so lothe to lende: for I care not
for dealing in the trade any more. What pleasure
were it to me to maime or mangle this Gentleman
for mine owne: truly I had rather if I could well
spare so much, to giue it him outright, so should
I sustayne no reproch my selfe: nor he be endamaged in the distresse of the law. Yet for your
sake, I care not if I lende him so much: so that
you wyll stande bound vnto mee, as straytlie as
hee shall.

Syr (quoth *Rodolfo*) for the credit of the Gentleman, I dare wage all that I am woorth, and for the payment thereof, I dare stand to the perill, deliuer you the money, and if the debt be not discharged before, or at the aboue named day: I will loose all my Landes, beside the best lym of my body. Well (quoth *Truculento*) this is the bonde, if by the first day of the month ensuing, the whole sum be not restored: eache of your Lands shall stand to the endamagement, besides the losse of bothe your right eyes, are you content to stand to this bargayne? Yea (quoth they bothe) and that right wyllingly.

With that he departed to fetche the money, then quoth *Strabino* to his freende. Dyd euer man see a more extorting villayne then this? Is not our Landes sufficient to glut vp his greedinesse? But that each of our eyes must stand to the hazard? Oh myserable myser, oh egregious cormorant, surely the iust iudgement of God, wyll reward him for his wickednesse. Well, cease (quoth *Rodolfo*) no more woordes, *Lupus est in fabula*, little sayd is soone amended.

Then comes *Truculento*, wylling them to tell out theyr money, and then to set their handes to his Byll, which beeing doone: he delyuered fortie Duckattes more to *Rodolfo*, to carie his Syster for a token from him, saying. Desire her to esteeme of the gratefulnesse of the gyft, more then the quantitie dooth amount vnto, and tell her, that in lyfe or death I am hers at commaund.

Your courteous token (quoth *Rodolfo*) shall be delyuered, and your message ministred, with as much expedition as possibilitie wyll permitte, and thus thanking you a thousand tymes for your

Brotherlyke beneuolence, I committe you to the
custody of the heauenly Creator. The lyke wishe
I you (quoth he) desiring you to remember the
bargaine wherin you are bound.

After that Rodolfo *and* Strabino
had borrowed the money of Signor Truculento,
*they departed to their lodgings, and in the morning
goe and buy the ritch Iewell, which* Strabino
presenteth to Signor Giorolamo Ruscelli,
the Father of Cornelia, *and obtayneth
promise that he shall haue her
in marriage.*

Cap. 6.

RODOLFO in the morning, repayreth to the
Chamber of his assured *Strabino*, where beeing entred, he found him in his study at his Booke,
awayting his company to goe about their busi-
nesse. *Strabino* (quoth he) let your Bookes a
whyle be left: and frame your selfe to furder your
fancie, let be the solemnesse you vse in your study:
for you are lyke to purchase a double delyght, the
tyde taryeth no man, and when we are assured of
our wished Iewell: then may we deferre the tyme
as long as we lyst. Wherefore, my selfe desyrous
to hasten in our enterprise, and also to prooue the
doubt of a dreame, I desire the more to make an
ende of this matter. Quoth *Strabino*, hath a

dreame driuen you in any such doubt, or haue you seen a fancie in your sleepe, which you shall prooue effectuous now you are waking: if it shall like you to tell me the trueth, I will define thereon as well as I can.

To trifle the tyme in talke (quoth *Rodolfo*) may let our labour, and beside, to shew you the effect of the same: would cause you to delude me, wherefore I will let it alone tyll we returne, and if by the way it prooue to perfection (as my desire is of God it may not) truly I wyll tell you. They take theyr way downe by *Signor Truculentos* doore, where he sawe the Saint sitting which all night was in his vision, no further could he goe he was so faynt, but stoode leaning on the brest of his freend *Strabino,* at last he burst foorth in these woordes, saying.

O my *Strabino,* but that you are my freend, and one whom I doo highly make accoumpt of: I should doubt to discouer the cause of my dollor, and feare to display my so sodayne passions, yet seeing your selfe hath tasted like torment, and haue borne out the bruntes which now I abide: the bolder I may my secretes bewraye, and the surer demonstrate the cause of my care. Yet you will condempne me for my preter presumption, and may rightly controule me for my rashe reprehension: yet iudge with indifferencie, and deale with me freendly, let olde faultes be forgotten, and penaunce clayme pardon. I see there is no stomacke so stoute: but looue will allay it, no courage so conquerous: but looue will conuince it, nor no heart so hautie: but looue can bring lowe: Euen so my selfe, who was a reiecter of looue, am now enforced to followe my fancie, and I who enuied against Women kinde: am now become a thrall to one my selfe.

With that for feare of beeing suspected in the open streete: they went theyr wayes about theyr other affayres, and as they were walking, quoth Strabino. I see deere freende, that the most learned Clarkes, are not the wisest, the most valiaunt, not the surest, nor the greatest boasters, the best per-fourmers, I perceyue you would haue beene in your deskant, before you knewe what pertayned to pricke Song. What say you nowe to Plautus woordes? What say you to all the matters where-with you charged me? Well, I will not replye so rashlie as you dyd: nor I will not giue you such colde comfort, as you vsed to me, but I wyll doo the best to make vp the matter, and my head to a halfepeny, I wyll bring it to effect.

I knowe it is Truculentos Daughter whome you desire, and she it is must cease your sorrowes: let vs first ende the matter we haue in hande, and then you shall see how I wyll compasse this geere. Rodolfo well satisfied with Strabinos promise: went and bought the Iewell which his Father so much desired, and there withall a fayre white Iennet of Spayne, and comming home: found his Father sitting at the doore, he entred, leauing Strabino to talke with him, who after he had sa-luted him in seemely sort: beganne his matters in this order as followeth.

To rip vp the cheefe occasions (woorthy Sir) that procureth me in what I can to pleasure you: would be ouer tedious to me in the telling, and somewhat troublesome to you in the hearing, wherefore letting them passe as remembred in minde, and recounting such matters as occasion dooth byd me: I first and formost present you with this rytch and sumptuous Iewell, wishing it so much woorth, as I could wyllingly bestowe.

When *Signor Ruscelli* sawe the Iewell, which so long he desired, and that his sonnes freend and Companion was the bestower of the same: he was ouercome with such exceeding ioy: that it is vnpossible for me to expresse. But when he had well viewed all about, and seene the sumptuous-nesse bestowed thereon: he aunswered *Strabino* to his great contentment.

If I should shew you (quoth he) how much this gyft pleaseth me, and besides, make manifest the good wyll I beare you: you would suppose I dyd but flatter you, and deeme my woordes of no true intent. Wherefore to driue you out of all such doubtes, and to make apparaunce of that I haue spoken: demaund of me what you shall deeme ex-pedient, and I vow to the vttermost to graunt your request.

With that *Cornelia* came to the doore, and seeing the Iewel in her Fathers hande: com-mended greatly the lyberalitie of her Brothers freende, and informing her Father to make him large amendes.

Syr (quoth *Strabino*) the Iewell giuen, byds me (vnder verdite of your lycence) craue an other Iewell, and this Iennet besides I giue you, wishing but to speede of that Iewell. What Iewell soeuer it be (quoth he) I haue, or any other thing, that may seeme to suffice you: on my credite and fidelitie, you can but aske and haue. *Strabino* stepped vp and tooke *Cornelia* by the hand, say-

ing: then giue me this Iewell in recompence of my
Iewell: so shall I be contented, and you nothing
iniured.

Syr *Strabino* (quoth *Signor Ruscelli*) the demaund you haue made is doubtfull, and the choyse
you haue chosen, nothing correspondent to
mine intent, her mariage is already made, and she
is giuen to one whose wealth is so woorthy, and
whose store so surpassing: that whyle she liueth,
she shall neede to lacke nothing. You are a young
Gentleman, youthfull and lyberall, and will spend
more in a day: then he in a yeere, he is warie and
wise, you youthfull and prodigall, therefore the
matche is otherwise determined, any thing else remayneth at your request. Syr (quoth *Strabino*)
you haue left a poynt open, and I haue a man to
enter, respect your play wisely, least you loose
the game outright. A promise may alwayes be
claymed for a due debt, and such a man as you
should neuer shrinke at his woord, I may clayme
this Iewell by a sufficient tytle: for that in your
promise you made no exception. Yea but *Strabino*
(quoth he) I meant you should haue desired some
other desert. But I meant (quoth *Strabino*) to
craue none other, so that you standing to the bargaine, and I lybertie to take what best lykes me:
this Iewell is mine, and your woorde a sufficient
warrant.

Besides, where you doubt my liuing is not sufficient to welcome such a Wife: I trust that the
patrimony my Parentes dooth allowe me, is more
then the dowrie you wyll make to her mariage.
Againe, if my lyberalitie, of you be dyslyked, and
the niggardly sparing of a worldly wretch so
much commended: I perceyue you preferre

rytches before a noble minde, and accoumpt more of vanitie, then you doo of vertue. *Mazeus* when he receyued his *Pretorship* of *Alexander:* in commendation of his munificence, vsed these woordes, My Prince *Darius* was euer but one man: but thou by thy lyberalitie, makest many *Alexanders*. *Scipio Africanus* neuer rode abroade, but he would vse such lyberalitie ere he returned: that of his greatest fooes, he would make his deerest freends. *Isocrates* wysheth *Nicocles* to be familliar with this excellent vertue, wylling him in his apparell to be gallant and glorious: and let his lyberalitie set foorth his magnificence. Then neuer disprayse lyberalitie, which is the cheefe ornament of a noble minde: but hate that worldly pleasure, enemie to all vertuous actions. I content my selfe to stand to her gentle iudgement, if she doo not regard me: I am content you shall refuse me, and if she lyke me not: I will let her alone.

What bargayne is betweene you twayne (quoth *Signor Ruscelli*) I knowe not, nor how you haue deuised the matter in hope to deceyue me, yet haue I seene no such familliarity, whereof I should accoumpt: nor any such likelyhood, that she will chuse you to her Husband. I am content to abyde her agreement, wherefore speake Daughter as your minde shall best serue you.

Then since deere Father (quoth *Cornelia*) it hath lyked you to graunt me my minde, in making my choyse, and that you will not be offended at my bolde behauiour: Syr *Strabino*, you are the man whome I most accoumpt of, and no other will I haue during lyfe.

When *Signor Ruscelli* perceyued it was come to that passe, and that his promise bound him to stand to her verdict: he sayd. Take heere then *Strabino*, the Iewell of my ioy, to quite your Iewell so lyberallie bestowed, and God graunt you such prosperitie whyle you liue together: as I wishe to mine owne soule, I speake vnfaynedly. The Nuptialles shall be celebrated when you thinke best, in the meane while I will take you as my Sonne, and you bothe as Man and Wife.

After much talke passed betweene them: out commeth the mournfull *Rodolfo*, rauished with such inward desyre, and tossed in such frantick fittes: as his pittious plight bewrayed the state of his sicknesse. *Strabino* taking leaue of his new found Father, and of his sweet Lady and wife *Cornelia:* went with him. And as they were going (quoth *Rodolfo*.) O my deere *Strabino*, needes must I goe, to knowe eyther of or on, her Father shall knowe the good will I beare her, and she shall perceyue I wishe her to my Wife. If I maye speede, I haue my desire, if not, the greater wyll be my distresse.

Ah Syr (quoth *Strabino*) how lyke you looue? Who shall controule you for following your fancie? A man knowes what his beginning is: but he knoweth not his ending. Brag is a good Dogge, whyle he will holde out: but at last he may chaunce to meete with his matche. In such like conference they came to the house of *Signor Truculento*, and who should open the doore but *Brisana* his Daughter, the Mistresse of *Rodolfo*, whome he saluted in very freendly sort. But euen so willing as he was to haue her to his Wife: she was as desirous to haue him to her Husbande. Heere was hote looue on bothe sides, and each of

them so farre in: that it was vnpossible for eyther
to gette out. *Rodolfo,* he in secrete telles *Trucu-*
lento such a flattering tale in his eare, howe his Sister had calmed her courage, and was content to
stand to her Fathers appointment: that the day
after the debt was discharged the mariage should
be made, so he for ioy of these newcome tydinges:
ioyneth them bothe hand in hand, to marie when
they will, and God giue them much ioy. Heere
were mariages soone made, and Wiues soone
wonne, I beleeue if I should sue for lyke succour:
I should perforce take longer space to speede.

Nowe is *Rodolfo* returned reioysing, and *Stra-*
bino right glad of his good successe, *Truculento*
presently hyes him to horsebacke, to goe wyll all
his freendes, to meete at his mariage.

When *Signor Ruscelli* knew how his sonne had
spedde, and by so fine a drift had deceyued
Truculento: the next morning marieth his sonne,
and *Truculentos* Daughter together, and *Cornelia*
and *Strabino* in the selfe same sort. What ioy was
heere on eyther side: iudge you that are maried
folkes and meddle in such matters, yet though I be
vnskilfull to define on such clauses: I must needes
suppose, that since each of them gayned, the thing
which they most desired: their ioy was not lyttle,
nor their pleasure lightly to be accoumpted of.

Strabino he with his sweete *Cornelia* passeth
the tyme pleasantly, and *Rodolfo* with his braue
Brisana lyueth at hearts ease and tranquilitie, so
that they thinke there is no other felycitie.

But now Gentlemen (as the auncient Prouerbe
is) after pleasure comes payne, and after mirth
comes myserie, and after a fayre and sunny day,

ariseth blustring windes and sharp showers: Euen
so to this passed pageant of pleasure, is annexed a
stratageme of sorrowes.

Truculento is returned from bydding his
Guestes, and hath heard of the hap which
chaunced in his absence, he comes as one bereft of
his wyttes, or as a man feared out of his fiue
sences, and vttereth this tale to *Signor Giorolamo
Ruscelli*. Syr, blame not my boldnesse, for that I
am constrayned, nor reprehend my rashnesse,
since I am so misused, I thought more credite had
consisted in your auncient heart, and that you
would not haue dissembled with any such double
dealing. Dyd not you perfectly promise I should
matche with your Daughter, and that no one
should gayne her but only I? Did not I giue your
Sonne my Daughter on the selfe same condition?
And haue you in my absence maryed her to an
other? Not contented with matching my Daughter with your Son, I beeing not present: but to goe
and play such a Parasites part. Well, well, I doubt
not but to deale so sharply with some: that they
shall wishe they neuer had maried my promised
wife.

Fewe woordes and sweete Syr (quoth *Signor
Ruscelli*) threatned folkes liue long, and angrie
men are subiect to many sorrowes, I gaue you no
other consent, then on my Daughters agreement,
and when I mentioned the matter: I styll found
her contrarie. Wherfore you must pacifie your
selfe, there is no other remedy, and learne to make
a vertue of necessity, for sure your lucke was still
turned to losse. And whereas my Sonne hath
matched with your Daughter: I deeme you are
not greatly to finde any fault, but rather may be

glad she hath sped so well, for the day hath beene
he might haue had her betters. Wherfore if you
seeme to chafe your selfe vpon so lyght occasion,
and that you will not be contented, we offering
you such courtesy: meddle in no more matters
then you may, nor heape any more harmes on
your head, then you are wylling to beare. If you
set not a poynt by vs: we care not a pyn for you,
if we may haue your good will so it is: if not,
keepe your winde to coole your Pottage.

This aunswere made *Truculento* more mad
then he meant to be, and he flung foorth of doores
in such a fume: as though all the Towne would
not haue helde him.

On the morrow, he caused *Strabino* and *Ro-
dolfo* to be summoned to appeere before the
Iudge, for the payment of the money, which when
Cornelia and *Brisana* perceyued: they willed their
Husbandes in nothing to doubt, for that by their
industrie they should be discharged. *Cornelia* ap-
parelleth her selfe all in blacke like a Scholler, and
Brisana attyreth her selfe in the same sorte. After
dinner they appeered before the Iudge, where
Truculento appealed against them in this order.

❦ Signor Truculento *summoneth*

Strabino *and* Rodolfo *before the Iudge, for the debt which was due to him, where* Cornelia *and* Brisana, *by their excellent inuencions redeemeth their Husbandes, and* Truculento *at last seeing no remedy: falleth to agreement.*

Cap. 7.

MOST magnificent Iudge, tyme was (quoth *Truculento*) when firme affection, and pure zeale of freendshippe, mooued me to minde the destitute estate of these two Gentlemen, when as either they had not money to their contentment: or wanted such necessaries, as then was to them needefull. At which tyme (as the Lambe endaungered by the rauenous Woolfe, flyeth for sauegard to his folde, or as the Ship abiding the hazard of Fortune, and fearing the emminent daunger, posteth to some Porte, or hasteth to some Hauen in hope of succour): Euen so these twayne repayred to me, who beeing sufficiently stored of that which they wanted, and besides, willing to pleasure them, to their greater profite: committed to their custody, a certayne summe of money, which amounteth vnto fowre thousand Crownes. Nowe theyr necessite indifferently satisfied, and they beeing bound to delyuer the summe at a certayne daye: they haue broken theyr promise, which is open periurie, and falsyfied theyr faythes,

in not restoring the money. Wherefore, that all
Gentlemen may be warned by such wylfull offenders, and that God may be glorified in putting
them to punishment: I haue thus determined how
the debt shall be discharged. The rendring of the
money I doo not accoumpt of, ne wyll I be pleased
with twise as much restored: the breach of the
Lawe I meane to exact, and to vse rygor, where it
is so required.

The forfayture of theyr Landes, is the one part
of the penaltie, the losse of theyr right eyes the
whole ingenerall, now remembring the wofull
estate of theyr solitarie wiues, how in depriuing
theyr substaunce, they might be pinched by
penurie: I let theyr Landes remayne vnto them in
full possession, whereon heereafter they may liue
more honestly. I clayme theyr right eyes for falsi-
fying theyr faith: to mooue others regard howe
they make lyke rechlesse promises. So shall Iustice
be ministred without partialytie, they rightly
serued for infringing theyr fidelity: and my selfe
not thought to deale with crueltie.

Thus haue you heard the cause of my comming:
now giue iudgement as your wisedome shall
thinke most expedient. My freends (quoth the
Iudge) heere is no place to deale with partialitie,
heere is no roome where falsehood should be frequented, nor time in this place to deferre in trifling
affayres: but heere is simply Iustice to be
aduaunced, wrong rightly reuenged, and mercie
mildly maintayned. Wherfore, ere I beginne to
deale in this diuersitie, or that I seeme to contend
about this controuersie: I exhort you each one to
exempt double dealing, to flye forged fraude, and
to minister nothing malitiously, but on each cause

to way the matter aduisedly. Consider you come
to deale in matters of conscience, matters of your
owne mayntenaunce, and such thinges whereon
your credite consisteth, now you are not for
freendshippe to further falsehood, ne yet for mal-
ice to touch an vntrueth, but euen to deale so di-
rectly, to frame your matters so faithfully, and to
vse your selues heere so vprightly: that not so
much as a motion be made of any misorder. But
euery one to aunswere as occasion is offered, so
helpe you God and the contentes of this booke,
wherat they all kissed the booke. And then the
Iudge called *Strabino,* to shewe in what sort, and
after what order the money was borrowed, and
what promise there was betweene them.

Most mightie Iudge (quoth *Strabino*) trueth
neuer defameth his Maister, right repelleth all
proffered wrong, and vpright dealing disdayneth
all forged fraude, wherefore, neyther fearing the
force of his reuenging rigor, nor yet dismaying at
ought that is doone: I will tell my tale, reporting
nothing but trueth, and clayming no other courtesie then my desertes shall deserue.

Trueth is, my Father fayling to send me such
money, as serued to the mayntenaunce of my
studious exercise, and besides, wanting wherewith
to deale in waighty affayres: my freend and I
came vnto this Caterpyller, (so rightly may I call
him, neyther defacing his lycentious lyuing, con-
dempning his practised science, and cunning
handy craft, nor yet inuaying against any of his
honest behauiour: but commending his cut throate
conditions, in pinching the poore, to fyl vp his
own poutch.) Beeing come to this aforesayd
woorme of the world, (who eateth so many to the

bare bones, out of Lands and lyuing, to glut his greedy desire) we desired a certayne summe of money, which is no lesse then him selfe hath confessed, for a monthes space, and then to restore the same to the vnrightfull owner, who binding vs straytly in the losse of our Landes, and of each our right eyes: lent vs this aforesayd sum. Now in deede, we not minding the so short restoring of his due debt, for that necessary occasions was partly our hinderaunce: haue indamaged our selues in two dayes more, then the limmited time did amount vnto, for which time we will allow him to the vttermost he can aske, and his money to haue when him pleaseth. Now if your wisdome dooth not thinke we deale with him honestly and well: we will stand to what effect it shall like you to bring it.

My freend (quoth the Iudge) your reply is reasonable, you confesse your selfe indebted in that which he hath demaunded, and yeeld that you haue broken the band, wylling to make an amends, insomuch that you will satisfie the vttermost, which he may seeme to sue for: I can not chuse but accoumpt your woordes of good credite, in that your dealing dooth demonstrate no other. Now *Truculento*, you see the Gentleman graunteth him selfe guilty, since his earnest affayres dyd hinder the repayment of your debt to you due, now he hath the whole ready to restore, and beside, ouer and aboue this sum: will content you to the vttermost it shall please you to request. In my opinion you can reasonably require no more, if you doo: you shall but seeme to shame your selfe.

Syr (quoth *Truculento*) he that before my face

will vse such terrible tauntes, behinde my backe, would gladly brew my bane, he that in my presence will so spightfully reprooue me: in my absence would hang me if it were in his possibilitie. Dooth he demerit fauour: that so frowneth on his freend? Can he clayme any courtesie: that abuseth him selfe so disorderly? Or can he once pleade for pittie: that standeth in so great a presumption? Or you my Lord, desire me deale gently: with one who respecteth not gentillitie? No, the money is none of mine, ne will I haue it, his Landes I respect not, ne care I for them, and now his submission I way not, ne will I accept of it. You my Lord shall rather reape reproche by pleading on his part: then gayne any credite in maintayning so carelesse a creature. I driue my whole action to this issue, I plead my priuiledge vnto this poynt, and to this clause I am seuerely bent: I will haue the due which breach of promise dooth deserue, I will exempt all courtesie: and accoumpt of cruelty, I wyll be pleased with no ritch reward whatsoeuer, no pitty shall preuayle, rigor shall rule, and on them bothe I will haue Lawe to the vttermost.

Why *Truculento* (quoth the Iudge) respect you cruelty: more then Christian ciuillitie, regard you rigor more then reason. Should the God aboue all Gods, the Iudge aboue all Iudges, administer desert, which your sinnes hath deserued? If his fatherly affection, if his mercifull myldnesse, if his righteous regard, dyd not consider the frayltie of your fleshe, your promptnes vnto peryll, and your aptnes vnto euyll: how mightie were the myserie, which should iustly fall vpon you? Howe sharpe the sentence that should be pronounced against you, and howe rigorous the

reuenge, which should rightly reward you? Is this
the looue you beare to your brother? Is this the
care you haue of a Christian? The *Turke*, whose
tyranny is not to be talked of: could but exact to
the vttermost of his crueltie. And you a braunche
of that blessed body, which bare the burden of
our manifolde sinnes: howe can you seeme to
deale so sharply with your selfe? seeing you
should vse to all men: as you would be dealt withall. Yet to let you haue the lybertie of your demaund in Lawe, and you to stand to the Iustice
which heere I shall pronounce, let first your right
eye be put foorth in theyr presence: and then shall
they bothe abide lyke punishment.

For since neyther the restoring of your debt
wyll suffice you, nor yet the lyberall amendes they
are content to make you: I deeme it expedient you
should be pertaker of theyr paynes, so shall you
knowe if you demaund a reasonable request.
Howe say you, will you stand to the verdict pronounced: or take the rewarde which they haue
promised.

My Lord (quoth *Truculento*) neyther doo I
deserue to abide any such doome, nor they
woorthy to be fauoured with any such freendshippe, I may lawfully alleadge that you permit
partiality: and that you deuide not each cause indifferently, for to what ende should you seeme to
satisfie me with their woordes: when your selfe
perceyues how they are found faultie? And what
vrgeth you to vse such gentle perswasions: when
you see your selfe they deserue no such dealing?
If I had wylfully offended in any such cause, and
wyttingly broken in such sort my bonde: I would
be contented you should deliuer me my deserts,

so that you dyd minister nothing but Iustice. And
wherefore should you seeme to demaund the losse
of my eye who haue not offended: for sauegarde
of their eyes that haue so trecherously trespassed?
I am sure I go not beyond the breache of my
bande, nor I desire no more then they haue deserued. Wherefore obiect no more matters,
whereby to delude me, nor impute no occasions
to hinder my pretence, I craue Iustice to be
vprightly vsed, and I craue no more, wherefore I
will haue it.

Indeede my freends (quoth the Iudge) who
seeketh the extremitie, and vrgeth so much as his
wilfull minde dooth commaund him: his commission is very large, and his request not to be refused. Wherfore, since neither pittie can preuaile,
nor freendly counsayle perswade: you must ren-
der the raunsome that he dooth require, for we
cannot debarre him in these his dealings, nor we
can not chuse but giue our consentes. Therfore if
you haue any that will pleade your case in Law:
let them speake and they shall be heard, to further
your safety as much as we may.

My Lord (quoth *Rodolfo*) theyr courtesie is
ouermuch that will kneele to a Thystle, and theyr
beneuolence bountifull that will bowe to a Bram-
ble: Euen so we are farre foolishe to craue courtesie of such a cut throate, and more wytlesse then
wyse to meddle with such a wordly wretch. If
there be no remedy: we knowe the vttermost of
our paynes, yet we craue that these our Attorneyes, may haue such lybertie as Lawe will permit.

With that *Truculento* fared like a fiend, and
curssed and banned like a Diuell of hell, (quoth

he) my Lord, you deale with me discourteously: when the Lawe is come to the passe to let them haue theyr Attorneyes.

Syr (quoth the Iudge) you haue vsed all this whyle your Attorneyes aduise, and they haue aunswered simply of them selues, now since you the Plaintife haue had this prerogatiue: it is reason the Defendaunts should demaund their due. It may be that their Attorneyes may put you to such a plundge: that you shall haue small occasion to bragge of your bargayne: wherefore let them speake.

Then *Brisana* (*Truculentos* Daughter) began in this order to pleade for her auayle. Admit my Lord (quoth she) that I come to such a person as this partie, to borrow the lyke sum of money, binding me in the selfe same band, to restore the money to the same party of whome I had it. Well, the time expyred, I come to deliuer the due to the owner, he being not at home, nor in the Citty, but ridden foorth, and vncertaine of his comming: I returne home to my house, and he him selfe comes out of the Countrey as yesterday. Now he vpon some seuerall spight or malicious intent: sueth me in the Lawe, not demaunding his due, nor I knowing of his ariuall. Am I to be condempned for breaking the Lawe: when the partie him selfe hath deferred the day?

How lyke you this geere *Truculento?* you haue now an other Pigeon to pull, and heere is one wiser then you were beware. Can you condempne this partie, not demaunding your due, nor beeing at home when it might haue beene discharged? And making the bande to be restored to your selfe?

My Lord (quoth *Truculento*) though I was not at home: my house was not emptie, and though I was away, if it had beene restored: it stoode in as good effect as if it had beene payd to me. Wherefore it is but follie to frame such an allegation: for my Receyuer in my absence dooth represent my selfe.

Well (quoth *Brisana*) admit your seruaunt in your absence, standeth in as full effect as your selfe, and admit the debt had beene discharged to him, if wylfulnesse had allured your seruaunt to wandering, and that he had departed with the debt he receyued: you returne and finde it styll in your booke, neither marked nor crossed, as if payment had not beene made, you wyll let your seruaunt slyp with his offence: but you wyll demaund the debt agayne of me.

Tush (quoth *Truculento*) this is but a tryfle, and your woordes are now to be esteemed as winde, you should haue restored the summe to my seruaunt: and I would not haue troubled you in any such sort, for there is no man that vseth such follie: but he will see the booke crossed before he depart. Therefore you doo but trouble tyme with mentioning such matters: for your redemption is neuer the neere.

Well then Syr (quoth she) you will thus much allow, that at the deliuery: the bande should be restored, and if I had delyuered the money to your seruaunt: I should haue respected my bande tyll yesterday, for your seruaunt had it not to delyuer: and I would not pay it before I had my bande. Ah *Signor Truculento* (quoth the Iudge) he toucheth you to the quick now, how can you reply to this his demaund? In deede I confesse

(quoth he) my Cubborde kept the bande tyll I returned, but yet noting the receyt in the booke,
would haue beene sufficient tyll my comming
home.

With that *Cornelia* stepped vp, saying. Since
(*Signor Truculento*) you will neyther allowe the
reasonable aunsweres he hath made, nor be content to abide my Lord the Iudges verdict: receyue
the raunsome you so much require, and take bothe
their eyes, so shall the matter be ended. But thus
much (vnder verdict of my Lord his lycence) I
giue you in charge, and also especially notifie, that
no man but your selfe shall execute the deede, ne
shall you craue any counsayle of any the standers
by. If in pulling foorth their eyes, you diminishe
the least quantitie of blood out of their heads, ouer
and besides their only eyes, or spyll one drop in
taking them out: before you styrre your foote,
you shall stand to the losse of bothe your owne
eyes. For that the bande maketh mention of nothing but their eyes, and so if you take more then
you should, and lesse then you ought: you shall
abide the punishment heere in place pronounced.
Nowe take when you will, but beware of the bargayne.

Truly (quoth the Iudge) this matter hath beene
excellently handled, it is no reason if you haue
your bargayne: that you should hinder them with
the losse of one droppe of blood, wherefore I pronounce no other Iudgement, shall at this tyme be
ministred.

Now was *Truculento* more mad that he could
not haue his hearts desire, for that he knewe he
must needes spyll some blood, it could not be other
wyse chosen, wherefore he desired he might haue

his money, and so let all other matters alone. Nay (quoth the Iudge) since you would not accept of it when it was offered, nor would be contented with so large a promise: the money shall serue to make them amendes, for the great wrong which you would haue offered. Thus in my opinion is Iudgement equally vsed, and neyther partie I hope will be miscontented.

Truculento seeing there was no remedy, and that all the people praysed the Iudgement so woorthily: accepted *Rodolfo* for his lawfull sonne, and put him in possession of all his lyuinges after his disease. Thus were they on all partes verie well pleased, and euerie one accoumpted him selfe well contented.

If now this homely Historie may seeme to suffice you: in recompence of my costes, I craue nothing but your courtesie. You shall haue the rest as possibilitie can permyt me, and I remayne your freend to pleasure you in ought to my power.

Take this in meane tyme, though too short
to be sweete, and thus I byd *Euphues*
hartily welcome into *England*.

Honos alit Artes.

FINIS.   A. Munday.

EMENDATIONS

EXPLANATORY NOTES

INDEX OF PROVERBS, ETC.

LIST OF EMENDATIONS

[The numbers, as in the Explanatory Notes following, refer to pages and lines in the present edition (8:3 = page 8, line 3); *m* designates a reading in the marginal glosses. In each entry, the emended reading is followed, after a bracket, by the reading of the 1580 quarto.]

8:3	is] it
8:10	courteous] courteons
15:27	disstressed] dis-/ stressed
17:5	∧as (perchaunce)] (∼ ∧∼)
20:1	spent] spend
21:16	me] *om.*
21:20	(they ∧beeing] ∧∼ (∼
22:9	she).] ∼)∧
27:8*m*	Abraham.] ∼∧
28:12	*Zelauto.*] *cw on sig.* **C3**ᵛ; *om. at the top of the next page of text, sig.* **C4**ᵛ
28:20	∧quoth she∧] (∼ ∼)
30:7	vnderstanding] vnder-/ ding (*corr. in errata*)
32:14*m*	*Englyshe*] *Enlyshe*
34:8	there. He] ∼, he
36:6	magnanimitie] magnaminitie
36:8	pregnantest] pregnanst
36:28	*Timantes*] *Timon* (*corr. in errata; emended also in marginal gloss*)
37:27*m*	Praxilla,] ∼∧
37:28*m*	Cleobulina,] ∼∧
38:13	∧if . . . be∧] (∼ . . . ∼)
38:17	*Zelauto*] *zelauto*
39:6	me] *om.*
39:14	*Zelauto*] *zelauto*
41:13*m*	Orcades] Orca-/ cades
45:29*m*	*his gifts*] *hts kifts*
46:7	of] of/ of

47:25–26	nothing] no-/ nothing
49:19	dye,] ~.
55:2	*but*] *bnt*
63:22	Wyldnesse] Wyl-/ desse
64:3	barter] bater
64:8*m*	*mischeefe,*] ~ˇ
64:25	then] then then
64:28–29	consideration, always remembred,] ~ (~ ~)
66:8*m*	and] *om.*
67:30	Gentlewoman] Genlewoman
68:30*m*	Zelauto,] Zelau.
69:3	receyue] receyne
78:13	fare,] ~.
78:14*m*	*Gentleman*] *Gnetle / man*
78:35	you] yon
79:24–25	aduenture: how] ~? How
79:32	ˇI . . . selfeˇ] (~ . . . ~)
81:21	patience] patienee
82:29	selues] selnes
84:12	anoye] any
87:35	in] *om.*
89:13	ˇin . . . victoryˇ] (~ . . . ~)
92:17	force] fore
93:21	Kinsfolke] Kinskolke
95:33	frankly] franke
99:22	vertuous] verteous
102:14	dolefull syght] dolesyght
114:12	serued.] ~ˇ
115:1	*Pescara*] *Peseara*
125:12	it.] ~,
125:18	*offereth*] *offereh*
125:31	ensue, always prouided,] ~ (~ ~)
126:29	protestation?] ~ˇ
127:13	as you] as your
128:19–20	in your] in you
128:26	to] to/ to
129:23	ˇAh] (~
130:8	vnrewarded.] ~ˇ
131:33	she).] ~)ˇ
132:5	she).] ~)ˇ
132:6	Why] why

132:7	she).] ~)∧
133:12	if my] ifmy
135:11	*Danæus*] *Dauæus*
138:29	that] yᵉ (*i.e.*, the)
138:34	straunge] strauuge
141:33-34	*Peripatetions*] *Peripa-/ tions*
145:8	misvsed] mis-/ vsed
145:20	that] that/ that
146:18	thystle.] ~∧
146:24	sayd.] ~∧
147:18	eloquence] eloqnence
148:34	no] *om.*
149:33	glorie,] ~?
151:34-35	age, for . . . yeeres, ∧for] ~) ~ . . . ~, (~
157:30	proffered, it] ~. It
159:19	egregious] egregrious
160:1	beneuolence,] ~.
160:26	dreame,] ~.
166:10	with] wich
166:24	beginning] begin ning
167:7	newcome] new-/ come
167:9	ioy.] ~∧
167:14	successe] succcesse
170:27	satisfied] satissied
171:30	rightly] righly
180:22	though too] thoughtoo

3:2–3 Edward de Vere, *Earle of Oxenford*] To Oxford (1550–1604), whose patronage he acquired perhaps through Charlewood or John Allde, Munday had already presented a copy of his now lost "*Galien of Fraunce*" (1578 or earlier) and dedicated *The Mirrour of Mutabilitie* (1579). It was probably on Oxford's advice that he went to Rome in 1578 (Celeste Turner Wright, *SP*, LVI [1959], 155). B. M. Ward, *The Seventeenth Earl of Oxford* (London, 1928), p. 187, takes the wording of the title page of *Zelauto* ("A. M. Seruaunt to the . . . Earle of Oxenford") to mean that Munday was now attached to the earl's household. A coat of arms and the Oxford motto ("Vero nihil verius") appear on the leaf following the title page.

3:10–23 *After that . . . same place*] The English prince is Edward (Don Duardos); Primaleon's father is Palmerin d'Oliva, and his half-brother is Palmendos (Polendos). Munday refers to incidents of the Spanish *Primaleón* (1512), which he subsequently translated (from the French) as *Palmendos* (1589) and *Primaleon of Greece* (in three parts, of which the first two are dated 1595, 1596; no copy of the first edition of Part III has survived).

6:19 Palmerin *of England*] "A booke intituled *the historie of* Palmerin *of Englande*" was licensed to Charlewood on 13 February 1581 (Arber, II, 388), and Parts I and II were apparently published between 1581 and 1588 (see Gerald R. Hayes, *Library*, 4th ser., VI [1925], 59); the earliest extant editions are dated 1596.

7:26–8:3 *Euphues . . . Lilly*] Lyly's *Euphues and His England*, licensed on 24 July 1579 (Arber, II, 357) and published in 1580 with a dedication to Oxford, was apparently already in print (but see p. vii, n. 1, above).

18:19 sayth *Tullie*] *De Partitione Oratoria*, XXIII.81.

20:3 *Malè . . . dilabuntur*] From Cnaeus Naevius (it is Naevius' unassigned fragment 38 in the Loeb Library *Remains of Old Latin*), quoted by Cicero in *Philippics*, II.xxvii.66.

21:16–17 dispoyled me of] The 1580 "dispoyled of" makes sense if it is read as "despoiled off" = "took off." But the *NED* ("despoil," *v*.3.d.) gives but two examples, both dated 1483; and at 24:4, in a similar context, Munday's text reads "spoyled me of."

25:24 *Primero*] A gambling card-game; but Ursula, who will satisfy Zelauto's need in "a greater matter" than money (25:24–25), apparently speaks metaphorically.

27:2–3 *Cæsar . . .* Commentaries] *De Bello Gallico*, VI.23.

27:8–13 *Abraham . . . Lot . . . Rahab*] Genesis 18, 19; Joshua 2–6.

29:1 *The Song*] Reprinted by A. H. Bullen in *Poems, Chiefly Lyrical, from Romances and Prose-Tracts of the Elizabethan Age* (London, 1890), pp. 74–75.

37:19 *Marques Vitelli*] Ciapino Vitelli, the Italian militarist (d. 1576), served Philip II in Africa and Holland (*Biographie universelle ancienne et moderne*, nouvelle édition [Paris, n.d.], XLIII, 652), and negotiated some financial dealings between Spain and England in September 1570 (Thomas Wright, *Queen Elizabeth and Her Times* [London, 1838], I, 379). Munday's anecdote foreshadows the famous incident of 1597 when Elizabeth upbraided the Polish ambassador *extempore* in Latin (see Wright, II, 478–80).

37:27 (and *m*) *Eriune*] Probably Munday read of the Lesbian poetess Erinna (or saw her name listed) in some text in which the first *n* of her name was turned upside down.

38:5–7 *Let all . . .* Elyzabetha.] Possibly not a part of the text proper, but the caption for a woodcut that occupies the rest of the page (sig. E1ʳ) showing Elizabeth in a horse-drawn carriage, Fame with her trumpet, four mounted knights, and some bystanders. (The woodcut appeared earlier, with an enthroned skeleton representing death that was subsequently cut out, in Bateman's *The Trauayled Pylgrime*, sig. M2ᵛ: see the note to 61:18, below.)

39:22–23 Shyp wherof I haue spoken.] Followed (on a new page, sig. E2ᵛ) by six lines of verse above a woodcut of an armed ship (used earlier in the book on sig. D3ʳ, after the text of 32:30):

In Countryes cause, I mount vpon the Seas,
    with shiuering shot to daunt my furious foe:
It dooth me good all strife for to appease,
    to keepe my Land free from all forrain woe.

God saue my Prince, that keepes a Nauy huge:
In time of neede to stand for her refuge.

48:10 reuolt] Probably an error for "revoke" (one
form of which in the sixteenth century was "reuolk").

50:3–4 *Forsan . . . iuuabit*] *Aeneid*, I.203.

50:5–6 *Dulce . . . malorum*] Perhaps based on the
Euripides fragment 131 in Johann Augustus Nauck,
Tragicorum Graecorum Fragmenta (Lipsiae, 1856):
ἀλλ' ἡδύ τοι σωθέντα μεμνῆσθαι πόνων.

51:13 as gallant a discourse] That is, Part III of
Zelauto.

52:7–8 one of them in especiall] Munday of course
praises his patron, the Earl of Oxford.

55:7   Argantus] A reference to Arganthonius, a king
of Tartessus in Spain who lived (according to different
accounts) either 120 or 300 years.

57:14 Honos alit Artes] Munday's Latin motto appears six times in *Zelauto* (on the title page, at the end
of each of the three parts, and on the separate title pages
for Parts II and III), and on the title pages of several
later works by him. It comes from Cicero (*Tusculan
Disputations*, I.ii.4), perhaps by way of Erasmus (see
Richard Taverner, *Proverbes or Adagies with Newe
Addicions Gathered out of the Chiliades of Erasmus*
[1539], sig. D1ʳ). In *The Golden Aphroditis* (1577),
sig. A2ʳ, it is Grange's "lawful excuse" for lack of skill.

61:18 full of Pictures] Twenty-three woodcuts appear
in Parts I and II (but none in Part III). Most of them

had been used earlier in Stephen Bateman's *The Trauayled Pylgrime* (1569), a work that Charlewood had recently bought from its original publisher, Henry Denham (see Arber, II, 359—the entry for 31 August 1579). A few of the illustrations were altered by the deletion of a skeleton or a pair of wings, but generally they have little relevance to Munday's text. (A woodcut, for example, showing *three men* seated at a table in a garden appears in *Zelauto* on sigs. B2ᵛ, C2ᵛ, H4ᵛ—following 17:19, 25:13, and 68:25 in the present text—to represent Zelauto with Astraepho, with Ursula, and with his Persian host and hostess.) They are not otherwise noticed in the present edition unless accompanied by letterpress captions (see the notes to 38:5–7, 39:22–23, 65:19, 103:26).

65:15 aspectation] The word (= "expectation") is not in the *NED*.

65:19 *Heer* Zelauto . . .] Above the chapter heading, on sig. H3ᵛ, is the caption "*Zelauto* remooueth his *Thought* to haste out of England." and a woodcut showing an old man and a winged runner (used earlier in Bateman, sig. B2ᵛ, where the winged figure is similarly identified as Thought).

78:7 *Viuit . . . Virtus*] The maxim occurs in several English works of the 1570's and 1580's; see Hyder Edward Rollins, ed., *The Paradise of Dainty Devices* (Cambridge, Mass., 1927), p. 267.

80:19–20 *Vsque ad mortem*] A common phrase, appearing (among other places) thrice in Plautus, once in Terence, and seventeen times in the Latin Bible.

84:12 anoye] In the *NED*, the form closest to the 1580 reading ("any") is "anye"—found only, however, in the fourteenth century.

91:10 *Aglaurus*] Aglauros, or Agraulos, a *daughter* of Cecrops, threw herself from the Acropolis to save Athens.

102:14 dolefull syght] For the 1580 reading ("dole-syght"), perhaps "dole syght" is a preferable emendation, but the *NED* does not recognize "dole" as an adjective (except as a fifteenth-century form of "dull").

103:26 Monuments . . . Champion.] Followed by a page (sig. M3ᵛ) containing two lines of verse—"In life I wun the type of hye Renowne: / And now in death I weare dame *Honors* Crowne."—and a woodcut (used earlier in Bateman, sig. L3ʳ) showing two men, a woman, a skeleton, and several crowns and statues.

107:1–112:21 *The Author . . . Munday.*] In the unique extant copy of 1580, the last three leaves of sig. N are bound in the following order: N4 (unsigned, "The Author, to the curteous / *Readers*."), N3 (unsigned, "Astræpho. / A Delycate Deuise . . ."), N2 (signed "M.ij."—"*The Author.* / Courteous Gentlemen . . .")—as if the sheet were first folded lengthwise rather than (correctly) widthwise.

111:19–23 Diogenes . . . neuer be] The anecdote (Diogenes Laertius, *Lives of Eminent Philosophers*, VI.56) appears, among other places, in Nicholas Udall's *Apophthegmes . . . First Gathered and Compiled in Latine by . . . Erasmus* (1542), fol. 129ᵛ.

112:1 Aristotle sayth] *Nicomachean Ethics*, IX.iii.2.

113:8 apert] The 1580 reading is "a-/ pert"; both "apert" and "a pert" make sense.

122:16 *Ars . . . arte*] See the note to 131:3–4, below.

124:35 Wise *Cato* sayth] Perhaps in *Disticha Catonis*, II.4: "Iratus de re incerta contendere noli, / impedit ira animum, ne possis cernere verum."

131:3–4 *Qui simulat . . . arte*] *Disticha Catonis*, I.26.

135:6–8 *Iupiter . . . Danea*] Munday has, of course, confused Jupiter's encounters with Danea (as a shower of gold) and Leda (as a swan).

139:1–5 *Plautus* woords . . . *animus*] *Cistelleria*, 206–10.

139:9 *Antigonus . . . Demetrius*] In this context Munday is probably thinking of one of the exchanges between Demetrius and the elder Antigonus, his father. E.g., "learning that his son was sick, Antigonus was going to see him, and met a certain beauty at his door; he went in, however. . . . 'The fever has left me now,' said Demetrius. 'No doubt, my boy,' said Antigonus, 'I met it just now at the door as it was going away' " (Plutarch, *Demetrius*, XIX.5).

139:15 *Stesilia* the harlot] Stesileus, the youth loved by Themistocles and Aristides, is perhaps confused with Stesilea, a woman of Athens.

139:26 his sonne *Oristilla*] "Oristilla" (Aurelia Orestilla) was Catiline's mistress and wife. He is said to have killed a grown-up son by a former marriage in order to marry her.

144:6–7 *Admetus* . . . beloued] Alcestis, attired as a man, gained *her* "best beloued," who was, of course, Admetus (the story is told by Pettie, among others).

146:10 smoutched] Either an error or an unrecorded variant form of "smugged." In Deloney's *The Gentle Craft*, Part I (1597?), the word "smutched" (Q2–4) is misprinted in the earliest extant quarto (1627) as "smugged" (see *The Novels of Thomas Deloney*, ed. Merritt E. Lawlis [Bloomington, Ind., 1961], pp. 145, 367).

155:22 To deceyue him . . .] The rest of the fifth chapter and all of the sixth and seventh chapters, along with the title page to Part III and the author's note to "Courteous Gentlemen" at the end of Part II, are reprinted by Friedrich Brie, *Jahrbuch der Deutschen Shakespeare-Gesellschaft*, XLIX (1913), 109–21.

159:22 *Lupus* . . . *fabula*] A common proverb adapted from Terence, *Adelphi*, 537, and Cicero, *Letters to Atticus*, XIII.33a.

165:2–6 *Mazeus* . . . *Alexanders*] Plutarch, *Alexander*, XXXIX.6.

165:10 *Isocrates* wysheth *Nicocles*] *Ad Nicoclem*, 32.

175:27 deuide] Possibly an error for "decide"; under "divide," *v.*1.d., "determine, decide," the *NED* gives a single example dated 1596.

176:29 wordly] A legitimate spelling variant in Munday's time, but nevertheless probably an error here, since "worldly" is otherwise consistently used in the text.

INDEX OF PROVERBS, SENTENTIAE,
COMPARISONS, AND ALLUSIONS

[Munday's text is here modernized, given without quotation marks, and occasionally condensed without ellipsis dots. Parenthetical references designate proverbs and sayings entered in Morris Palmer Tilley's *A Dictionary of the Proverbs in England in the Sixteenth and Seventeenth Centuries* (Ann Arbor, 1950).]

Anthony Munday's ZELAUTO was set in Linotype Janson, and printed and bound by Kingsport Press, Inc., Kingsport, Tennessee. The typography and format were designed by Andor Braun.

The edition is limited to 1,500 copies
of which this is

Nº   855